UNCLE ARTHUR'S
BEDTIME STORIES
Seventeenth Series

With Every Good Wish

To ....

From ....

V17A1

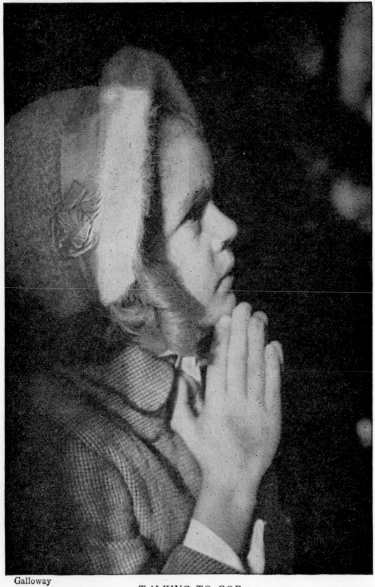

Galloway

TALKING TO GOD
(See story on page 83)

Uncle Arthur's

BEDTIME STORIES

(SEVENTEENTH SERIES)

BY ARTHUR S. MAXWELL

> "My son, keep thy father's commandment,
> and forsake not the law of thy mother. . . .
> When thou goest, it shall lead thee; when
> thou sleepest, it shall keep thee; and when
> thou awakest, it shall talk with thee."
> Prov. 6:20-22.

REVIEW AND HERALD PUBLISHING ASSOCIATION

TAKOMA PARK, WASHINGTON, D.C.

PRINTED IN U.S.A.

CONTENTS

PREFACE

DESPITE the war, the children must have their "Bed-time Stories." So, in the midst of the greatest con-flict of the ages, we send forth the seventeenth series of these little books to the children of the world.

Printed in the United States, in England, in Australia, and in many other lands, they will go farther and farther out, to the very ends of the earth. But where will they find the children this time? Many will be at home, of course, as usual, but others will be in strange homes and new surroundings. Some, perhaps, will be in air-raid shelters, and some in hospitals. May this year's stories be especially helpful to all.

To those who have never read "Bedtime Stories" be-fore, we would say that they are designed primarily as character-building stories; not only to amuse and entertain, but also to teach some great moral lesson. Every one has its message to the soul of childhood.

As always, the stories are definitely based on fact, many of them coming to us direct from children or their parents. Those which deal with answered prayer may be relied upon as absolutely true.

And so once more we send another series of "Bedtime Stories" on its mission to the children of many peoples and nations. That God may add His blessing to all who read them, parents and children, is the earnest prayer of

THE AUTHOR.

Georgie Didn't Lead the Singing Quite Like This!

Georgie Leads the Singing

IT was wartime. Bombs had been falling on the city.
Many people had been hurt, and some killed, and a
great number of houses had been blown to pieces.

Hospitals were crowded with the injured, and the doctors and nurses were busier than they had ever been before in all their lives.

Then one chilly winter morning a strange thing happened.

It was very early, between five and six o'clock, and
just getting light. A nurse, walking out of a certain big
hospital, saw what looked like a bundle of clothes on the
steps. Stooping to look at it more closely, she saw that
under all the wraps there was a little boy! He could not
have been more than four years of age, and as his sad brown
eyes looked up into hers, her heart was touched.

"What are you doing here at this time in the morning?"
she asked kindly.

The little boy did not reply, but pointed to a piece of
paper pinned to his coat.

The nurse unpinned it and began to read:

"My name is Georgie. I am not quite four years old.
My mamma is dead. My grandma is dead. Please look
after me."

"Oh, you poor little thing!" said the nurse, picking
Georgie up in her arms and hugging him close. "But
whatever shall we do with you?"

Marching up the steps with her strange bundle, the nurse went back into the hospital and tried to find out what should be done with Georgie.

The other nurses felt very sorry for him and wanted to do all they could to help, but the busy doctors said there wasn't time to spend on a case like this just now. He should be sent to an orphanage as soon as possible.

But the nurse who had found Georgie on the steps did not want him to go away so soon. She wanted to do something for him herself. So she hunted all around the wards to see if there was not some little corner where Georgie could be put without his being in the way or being noticed too much.

She searched and searched, but every place was full. At last, however, she came to the section of the women's ward where all the elderly women were cared for, and there she found a place just big enough to take a tiny cot for Georgie.

Naturally the old people were very much interested in the little boy who had been put in with them. They rather liked the idea, for it gave them something new to talk about. Then, too, Georgie was very good and quiet and didn't bother them, as some had been afraid he would.

That first night that Georgie was in the women's ward, the nurse who had found him came to tuck him in and bid him good night. As she was doing so, Georgie spoke to her.

"Me want to say mine prayers," he said, looking up solemnly into her face.

The nurse was so surprised. How, she wondered, did a little boy like this, barely four years of age, left destitute on the hospital steps, know anything about saying his prayers? He must have had a good mother, and no doubt a good grandmother, too.

"All right, dear," she said. "You may say your prayers if you wish. How shall we begin?"

"Shut your eyes," said little Georgie.

The nurse smiled, but obeyed.

"Put your hands together," said Georgie, and again the nurse did what she was told.

"Now we are ready," said Georgie, and he began to pray.

This was his little prayer, just as he prayed it:

> "Jesus, tender Shepherd, hear me,
> Bless Thy little lamb tonight.
> Froo the darkness be Thou near me,
> Keep me safe till mornin' light.
>   Amen."

Georgie opened his eyes just in time to see the nurse bending down to kiss him.

"Me sing that in the mornin'," he said.

"All right, dear," said the nurse. "You shall."

And in the morning Georgie began to sing his prayer. He sang it on and off all day, and everybody thought it was very sweet and beautiful.

Then one night the air-raid sirens sounded, and their dreadful wail struck fear into all hearts, though everyone tried to be very brave.

The bombers were coming again, with their grim loads of death and destruction.

All lights were put out, and the ward was very dark, the only light coming from the reflection of the search-lights on the cloudy sky.

Soon the bark of the antiaircraft guns could be heard.

This was followed by the distant boom of falling bombs. It was getting nearer and nearer, and the elderly women put their heads under the bedclothes as though to shut it all away.

Then suddenly there was a terrific noise as a bomb fell close by, right in the courtyard of the hospital. The whole building rocked. Every window was smashed. Even the wooden casings were blown into millions of little pieces which, together with the broken glass, were strewn all over the ward.

The women screamed in fright, and one of them died of heart failure.

Poor little Georgie, who had been asleep when the bomb exploded, woke with a terrible start and began to cry out: "Me want my grandma! Me want my grandma! Somebody light the dark! Somebody light the dark!"

Just then the nurse came running into the ward, and, picking her way through all the debris, came at last to Georgie's cot.

"Are you all right, Georgie?" she asked anxiously.

"Me want my grandma!" cried Georgie. "Somebody light the dark!"

The nurse picked him up in her arms and tried to soothe the poor little boy. Suddenly she had a bright idea.

"Georgie," she whispered, "sing."

"Don't want to sing," wailed Georgie. "Somebody light—"

"Yes, Georgie, sing," said the nurse. "Sing. It will help you. It will help everyone."

"What shall I sing?"

"You know. Your little song. Go on. Sing it, Georgie."

Georgie began.   In a faint, broken, tearful voice he
started to sing:

> "Jesus, tender Shepherd, hear me,
>   Bless Thy little lamb tonight.
> Froo the darkness be Thou near me,
>   Keep me safe till mornin' light."

And then a wonderful thing happened.

From away down the end of that pitch-dark ward came
the sound of another voice.   One of the elderly women
had begun to sing, too.   It was a quavering voice, but it
was singing.   And it was singing Georgie's song: "Jesus,
tender Shepherd, hear me."

And then another quavering voice joined in, and another
and another, until all down that ward, in the midst of the
darkness and the terror of that dreadful night, everybody
was singing the same lovely hymn.

As they sang, Georgie gathered courage and sang
louder and louder, while everyone felt better just to hear
him sing.   It seemed to bring God near.

Over and over again they sang the song until at last
the sound of the guns and the bombs faded away and
the lights came on again.

What a beautiful thing it was that Georgie did that
night!

Maybe one day you and I may be able to do something
like that, too.   Singing in the dark!   Singing courage and
cheer into hearts that are afraid and sad.

No matter how young you are, even if you are as young
as little Georgie, you can help to bring happiness to others.

Does not the Bible tell us that "a little child shall
lead them"?

English Children Leaving Their Homes in London to Escape the Bombs

Broken Bridges

M OTHER!" cried Horace, angrily, "why did you let those little refugee children come to stay in our house?"

"I don't think they will bother us too much," said mother. "I rather like them. They are different and interesting. We shall learn lots from them."

"I don't want to learn anything from them," cried Horace. "And I don't want them in this house. Why, mother, they will touch all my things and break my toys and smash my electric train! I know they will. Oh, it's terrible. Please send them away, mother."

"But where shall we send them?"

"Send them back to their homes, of course," said Horace hotly.

"But maybe they haven't any homes. Maybe their homes are all blown to pieces."

Horace looked thoughtful for a moment.

"Well, then, why don't their own mothers look after them?"

"They would like to, but they can't," said mother. "Their mothers are very sad that they cannot have their children with them. You see, dear, it is very, very dangerous; so we have been asked to mind their children for a little while until things get better."

"But, mother, do you want to have all these children running over our house and spoiling everything?"

13

"I didn't at first, dear, but I don't mind now. It is such a little for us to do, when others—hundreds and thousands of others—are losing everything they have. And do you know, Horace, something I read the other day helped me a great deal."

"What was that?" asked Horace.

"Oh, it was just a little story, darling. Such a sad little story. It is enough to make you cry."

"Tell me about it."

"It happened during the invasion of Belgium. The people were fleeing from their homes and hurrying southward toward France. In one little town there was a poor mother with her two little children. One was five and the other was eight. They hurried away from their home as fast as they could, and crossed the bridge over the river. Just as they reached the other side the mother remembered that she had not brought her identification papers with her— the papers that give one's name and address and other information, so the police will know who he is. Afraid that this might get her into trouble, she decided to leave the children for a few minutes and dash back to the house to get the papers. She reached the house, found the papers, and got back as far as the bridge. Just then there was a terrific explosion, and the bridge suddenly collapsed into the river. It had been blown up by the soldiers.

"The poor mother could see her two precious little ones on the other side of the river, but she could not get to them. She was so worried and frightened that she went raving mad."

Mother paused and noticed a tear in Horace's eye.

"Ever since I read that story," she said, "I have thought

about those two poor, lonely little children, unable to go back because of the broken bridge behind them, lost in the crowd of fleeing, terror-stricken people, and wandering on and on and on, looking for mother and home, but never finding them. I know that if I should meet them some-day, I should want to take them into my home and love them. Wouldn't you, Horace? I know you would."

"Oh, surely," said Horace. "I wish we could find them, don't you?"

"I do," said mother. "How we would look after them, wouldn't we, Horace? But as we can't find them, I thought we would do our little bit by looking after these other children who need help, too."

"I see," said Horace. "Maybe some bridges have fallen down behind them."

"They have," said mother. "They can never go back to the way of life they knew before. Everything will be different after this. And just for a little while we have a chance to make them happy. Shall we try?"

"Yes, of course we will," said Horace.

"I thought you would say that," said mother. "And what a blessing we shall get out of it ourselves! Once Jesus was talking about a lot of poor people with broken bridges behind them—the hungry, the thirsty, the strangers, the sick folk, the prisoners; and then, speaking of those who cared for them, and helped them to find their way home, He said that one day He would welcome them Him-self with these words: 'Come, ye blessed of My Father, inherit the kingdom prepared for you from the foundation of the world.' 'Inasmuch as ye have done it unto one of the least of these My brethren, ye have done it unto Me.' Matt. 25:34, 40.

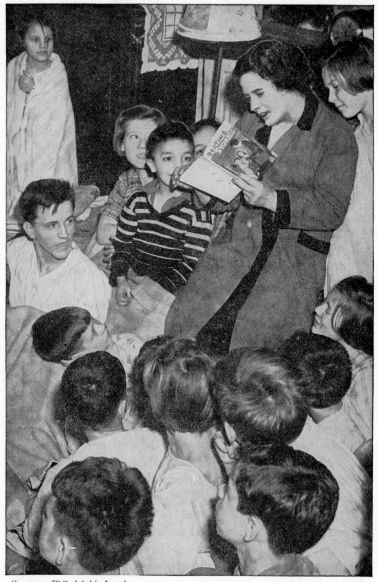

Reading Bedtime Stories to Homeless Children

16

Fire at the Orphanage

~~~~~~

BELIEVE it or not, but this really, truly happened in Philadelphia, in 1940.

At three o'clock one wintry morning, while nearly a hundred little boys and girls were fast asleep in a certain home for destitute children, somewhere in the building there was a spark, then a thin, innocent-looking little flame, followed by a tiny puff of smoke.

The house was on fire, but nobody knew.

Soon the flames had caught the floor boards, the rafters, the roof, and presently billows of smoke began to pour through the rest of the building.

At last someone thought he smelled "something burning" and, jumping out of bed, shouted, "Fire!"

There was no more sleep then. The staff woke up; the children woke up. Everybody woke up. And of course the first thought of those in charge was to get the children out of the building as fast as possible.

As for the boys and girls, they were very much excited, and some were much frightened. Here they were in a real fire for the first time in their lives. They could smell the smoke and hear the clatter of the fire engines rushing to put out the blaze.

No doubt some of them wondered whether they would get out in time, but bravely they hurried downstairs and out to safety.

Outside, however, it was bitterly cold, so cold, in fact,

that it even clogged the fire hydrants.   And here were a hundred children in their nighties!   They didn't have to shiver long, however, for they were quickly bundled up in blankets and hurried to a near-by house.   It was a doctor's residence, and here they were all received with open arms and served hot cocoa and cakes.

But just imagine a hundred children turning up in your house in the middle of the night!   What would you do with them?

Well, what do you suppose the woman of the house did to entertain this houseful of nervous, wriggling little visitors? Yes, she read to them.   You must have guessed that from looking at the picture.   But what did she read?

Look a little closer, and you will see.   In her hand is a copy of "Bedtime Stories," Eleventh Series, published in 1934.

It so happened that just as the woman was reading, in came a photographer of the Philadelphia *Inquirer*, and so we have this unique picture in the Seventeenth Series.

Now it may be that you have seen "Bedtime Stories" read in some unusual place, or at some unusual time like this.   If so, write and tell me about it.

Peter and the Pumpkin Seed

"MOTHER," said Peter one day, "I wish I could earn some money."

"Well, dear," said mother, "aren't you earning money now? You help me with little jobs, and I give you some pocket money every week."

"Yes, I know," said Peter. "But I mean some *real* money, like the grown-up people get. Wages, you know, mother."

"Oh, well, you will earn wages, I hope, when you grow up," said mother. "There's time enough for that."

"But I want to earn some now," insisted Peter. "Couldn't I go over to Farmer Johnson's and work for him?"

"Well, I suppose you could, if he would give you work. But you are only a little boy yet, you know. I doubt that he would be bothered with you."

"But won't you ask him?" pleaded Peter. "Just ask him. He can but say no."

At long last, after much persuasion, mother promised to see what she could do about it. And so it came about that it was agreed that Peter should spend one week of his holiday over at Farmer Johnson's, working each morning for an agreed sum, with play in the afternoon if he should do his work well.

Peter surely felt grown up when he set off with his little handbag containing his pajamas, hairbrush, toothbrush, and other things he needed, to go to work at the farm.

Farmer Johnson gave him a cheery welcome and set him to work at once doing odd jobs around the house.

Then one morning when the time came to start work Farmer Johnson told Peter that he had a very special task for him to perform that day.

"Peter," he said, "I want you to give me some real help this morning. Will you do something very important, and do it just as I say?"

"Oh, yes," said Peter, all excited. "Of course I will. What is it?"

"Come along with me," said Farmer Johnson, "and we shall soon find out."

First of all they went through the farmyard, where Farmer Johnson picked up a two-gallon pail full of pumpkin seed. Then together they walked out toward one of the fields, which was all ready for sowing.

Peter wasn't quite sure what it was all about, but guessed that his job would have something to do with that seed. Maybe he would have to carry the pail while Farmer Johnson sowed it.

"Now look," said Farmer Johnson. "Do you see this field?"

"Yes," said Peter, very meekly; and as he spoke he thought he had never seen such a big field in all his life.

"Well, now, I want you to sow this pumpkin seed in this field, and I want it done very carefully."

"Me?" said Peter.

"Yes, you," said Farmer Johnson. "I want you to walk down this first furrow and every twenty paces put in three seeds. Then when you reach the end of the first row, move over twenty paces and work your way back here. And continue until the pail is empty."

"Yes, Mr. Johnson," said Peter, proud to have a real job at last.

"You quite understand how I want it done?"

"Yes, I think so," said Peter. "Three seeds in each hole and twenty paces between holes."

"That's a good boy," said Farmer Johnson, with a smile playing around his weather-beaten face. "I think I'll be going now. Oh, by the way, as soon as you have finished you can go and have a dip in the swimming pool."

"Oh, thank you, thank you, Mr. Johnson," said Peter eagerly. "I won't be long."

"I wonder!" said Farmer Johnson to himself, as he said good-by and went away to his other tasks.

Meanwhile Peter set to work in earnest.

"Three seeds—twenty paces—three seeds—twenty paces," he murmured to himself as he moved slowly down the long, long row.

At last he reached the end and turned to look back to where he began. He could hardly see the spot, it was so far away.

Then he looked at his pail, and his heart sank.

It seemed just as full as when he had started!

"Why," he said to himself, "I've put in all those seeds, and yet it doesn't seem as though I have used any. I'll have to work harder still if I am ever going to get that swim."

So he moved over twenty paces and started on his long, slow journey back to where he began.

"Three seeds—twenty paces—three seeds—twenty paces."

Finally the second row was finished, and once more

he looked at his pail. He felt like crying. Truly the level of the seed had gone down a little, but, oh, so little.

He was getting just a wee bit tired now, and more than a wee bit hot, and as he looked at the huge pile of seed yet to be sowed he told himself that he never would get that swim Farmer Johnson had promised him if he continued this way.

Just then a very naughty thought came into his mind.

"I wonder if it would matter," he said to himself, "if I were to put four, or perhaps five, seeds in each hole? That would get the pail emptied so much faster. And Farmer Johnson would never know, not when the earth is covered over each hole."

He thought about it awhile, looked up at the sun, felt himself getting hotter and hotter, thought again of the swimming pool, and decided to do it.

Now his little chant was, "Five seeds—twenty paces—five seeds—twenty paces."

At last he came to the end of the third row, and turning, worked his way back to finish the fourth. But, alas, even then the pail seemed almost as full as before.

Tired and discouraged, Peter sat down.

"He shouldn't have given me such a big job to do," he said to himself. "He must have known I never could sow all this seed and still have a swim. He didn't mean me to have a swim at all. I know he didn't. But I daren't tell him that I couldn't finish the job. I'll go on and on and on till—but let me see, if it was all right to put five seeds in, why shouldn't I put in six or seven?"

And so he did, all down the next two rows.

"Twenty paces—seven seeds—twenty paces—seven seeds."

But even this did not empty the pail, and it was getting late now.

"I don't care," said Peter to himself. "I'm going to empty this pail whatever I do, and I am going to have my swim. I'll put a whole handful of seeds in every time."

He started off once more, tired and ill-tempered. And this time, with a certain viciousness he muttered:

"Twenty paces—handful—twenty paces—handful."

At this rate, of course, the pail was soon emptied, and with great relish Peter turned it upside down and hurried away to the swimming pool.

But somehow the swim was no fun at all. He had a strange, uncomfortable feeling inside him. Just what it was, or why it was, he could not say. But it was there, just the same.

Farmer Johnson hailed him and asked if he had finished the job.

"Oh, yes," called Peter, "all done;" but again that strange feeling bothered him.

"Good for you," said Farmer Johnson; but the words didn't do Peter half the good they usually did.

That night he went home. Mother asked him how he had enjoyed himself, and he said, "All right;" but inside himself he felt that it was not all right. He kept worrying about those pumpkin seeds; and suddenly it dawned on him that they would all come up!

Until that moment he had never thought about such a terrible thing's happening. Now he went hot and cold all over. Then he got on his knees beside his bed and asked God to kill some of the seeds at least, and not let them grow.

But they were growing even as he prayed. In a few days they were all above ground—all of them—every single one of them. And just then Farmer Johnson took a little walk to find out why it was that Peter had finished his job so much sooner than he had expected him to.

He smiled again, a strange little understanding smile.

They didn't meet again—Peter and Farmer Johnson— until the next time they went to church.

Now it so happened that Farmer Johnson went in one door and Peter went in the other door, and suddenly, right in the middle of the aisle, they came face to face.

Peter thought it was the day of judgment. If he could have, he would have turned and run, but something kept him riveted to the spot. He could see nothing but Farmer Johnson and behind him millions and millions of pumpkin plants. His lip began to quiver.

Farmer Johnson saw and understood. He had a kind heart, and he knew at once that Peter had learned his lesson.

"Don't cry," he whispered, as he came very close to Peter's ear. "Just remember that the seeds you sow in life always come up. 'Whatsoever a man soweth, that shall he also reap.'"

He squeezed Peter's hand in forgiveness, and Peter wished that he could go out of church right then and there and sow that field all over again.

Why Victor Slept So Well

THAT story about Peter and the pumpkin seed reminds me of another boy who wanted to go to work on a farm. I don't know his real name, but let's call him Victor, for he surely deserves a good one.

In the hope of getting work, Victor had gone to a big cattle show, where farmers from miles around came in to display their animals, inspect their neighbors' horses and cows, and quietly keep their eyes open for suitable men and boys to help them.

By and by one of the farmers came over to the group of lads among whom Victor was standing, and looked them all over very carefully.

"Want work?" he inquired.

"Yes," they chorused.

Then his eye caught sight of Victor, and somehow he was drawn to his open, honest, sunburned face.

"How about you, son? Do you know anything about farmwork?"

"I can sleep on windy nights," said Victor.

"What do you mean?" asked the farmer shortly.

"I can sleep on windy nights," replied Victor calmly.

"The boy's stupid," muttered the farmer, walking away. But Victor's strange words kept ringing in his ears. "I can sleep on windy nights," the farmer muttered to himself. "What on earth does the lad mean?"

A little later he came back to the same group. Victor

25

was still there, good-looking and honest-looking as ever. The farmer decided to try again. Once more he asked Victor to tell him what he knew about farming, but again he received the same strange reply: "I can sleep on windy nights."

"Well," said the farmer in exasperation, "you had better come along anyway, and we'll see what you can do."

So Victor accepted the job and went off to live on the farm. His work was good, and the farmer was pleased with him. But one night something happened.

It was late, and everybody had gone to bed and to sleep. Presently a heavy gust of wind in the trees awakened the farmer, and in an instant he was on his feet. He sensed immediately that a storm was coming up, and his first thought was for his cattle, his haystacks, and his barns.

Rushing into Victor's bedroom, he found the boy fast asleep.

"Wake up, wake up!" he cried.

But Victor slept on.

"Wake up, I tell you!" he shouted, becoming more angry every minute. "Can't you hear the wind?"

Still Victor slumbered.

"I'll fire him in the morning for this, I will," stormed the farmer as he hurried out of the room and down into the farmyard.

But here another surprise awaited him.

No doors were banging in the boisterous wind. All were tightly closed and barred. He opened one and peered into the cow barn. Every animal was in its place.

But what about the haystacks? he wondered. They must be blown to pieces by now. But they were not. In fact, so carefully had someone covered them that not a wisp of hay had been lost.

Through the darkness and the blinding rain the farmer stamped around his property, expecting every minute to find something wrong, but always finding everything right.

At last, dripping wet, he returned to the house. Going upstairs to Victor's room, he looked in. The boy was still sound asleep.

As the wind continued to howl around the house the farmer recalled the mysterious words: "I can sleep on windy nights." Suddenly he understood.

The boy had done his work so faithfully that there was nothing for him to worry about. He could sleep in a hurricane or an earthquake.

Victor kept his job.

Anne Shriber

How Much Does He Love His Daddy?

How Much Love?

30   HOW MUCH LOVE?

THIS is just a simple little story, but it's very sweet just the same. I think you will like it, and I know your daddy will!

One particular daddy I know had been trying to find out just how much his little boy Francis really loved him, and Francis would keep saying, "Heaps and heaps," and, "Lots and lots," and, "Bushels and bushels."

Just to tease him, daddy said that that wasn't enough; so finally Francis threw his arms around daddy's neck, hugged him ever so tightly, and said that *that* ought to answer his question properly.

By and by, when daddy was reading, having almost forgotten the fun they had just had together, Francis called him.

"Come over here, daddy; I want to show you something."

"Sorry, dear, I'm busy now."

"Oh, do come," urged Francis. "It's something very special."

"I'm reading," growled daddy good-humoredly.

"But you must come," said Francis. "I want to ask you something. Really I do."

"Oh, very well then," said daddy, putting his book down with a big sigh. "What is it now?"

Then he noticed what Francis had spread out on the floor.

"Here," he said, "what are you doing with my special map?"

Francis ignored the question and asked one of his own. "Is this a map of the United States?"

"Yes, of course it is," said daddy. "It's a road map. It shows the main roads all over the country."

"I thought it was," said Francis. "Now which was the road we traveled on last year, when we drove all the way over?"

Daddy thought about his book and groaned.

"That one, dear," he said. "That big red one."

"How long is it?"

"Oh, about two thousand miles. Maybe more than that."

"And, daddy, what are all these other lines? Red lines and black lines?"

"They are all the other roads."

"And where do they go?"

"Every place, I suppose."

"And how long are they?"

Poor daddy was stumped. He didn't know what to say.

"I don't suppose anybody knows," he said. "But I should say they are thousands and thousands and thousands of miles long."

"Might be millions and millions and millions of miles long?"

"Might be," said daddy in desperation.

"Well, then, daddy, that's how much I love you. All that lot!"

"Oh, you dear little thing," cried daddy, forgetting all about his book now and picking Francis up in his arms. "So all this time you have been trying to find some way of telling me how much you love me!"

And as he hugged Francis again, a little text came back to his mind: "As the heaven is high above the earth, so great is His mercy toward them that fear Him. As far as the east is from the west, so far hath He removed our transgressions from us. Like as a father pitieth his children, so the Lord pitieth them that fear Him." Ps. 103:11-13.

"Yes," he said to himself, "Someone else has been trying a long time now to tell us all how much He loves us, too."

"Wide, wide as the ocean,
High as the heavens above,
Deep, deep as the deepest sea,
Is my Saviour's love.
I, though so unworthy,
Still am a child of His care;
For His word teacheth me
That His love reacheth me,
Everywhere."

Harders, Artist

Is That You?

Is That You, God?

THEY had never had a telephone in the house before, and when at last the men came to put one in, it was a great day for everyone.

All the children watched with the deepest interest as a pole was set up, a wire was brought across to the house, and finally the magic instrument was connected.

Then, of course, everyone wanted to use it and telephone to all the friends in the neighborhood.

It was still being used late in the evening when the time came for little Alice, who had been watching everything most carefully, to be sent to bed.

"Don't forget to call me when you are ready to say your prayers," said mother.

"All right, mamma," said Alice, slowly moving toward the stairs. "But maybe I'll say them all by myself tonight."

"Just as you wish, dearie," said mother; "but I'll come if you call me, right away."

Alice disappeared and was soon engaged in the long, slow process of undressing, washing herself, putting on her nightie, and generally getting ready for bed.

Mother was beginning to wonder just how long it would be before she settled down for the night, when she heard an unusual sound. It seemed like the prolonged rattling of a doorknob.

Silently creeping to the sitting-room door, she poked her head outside and listened.

There it was again—Rattle, rattle, rattle.

Then a quiet, solemn little voice began to speak.

"Hello, hello! Oh, is that you, God? This is little Alice speaking. Isn't it nice we can talk to each other now? You are going to bless mamma and daddy and brother and sister? Is that so? No, you don't mean it? Really? Oh, please tell me, has Jesus found all His lost sheep yet? And, God—"

But just then mother coughed, or something else happened; anyway the voice ceased; there was another rattle of the doorknob, and a tiny, white-robed figure slipped into bed.

Alice had been telephoning her good-night prayer to God all in her own lovely little way.

Bless her little heart!

Maybe it would help us all if we were to think of prayer just as Alice did in her simple, childlike faith. Perhaps it will make prayer less formal, more friendly and personal.

Let us "telephone God" tonight.

On the Wings of the Wind

✦━━━〜〜〜〜〜〜〜〜〜〜〜〜〜〜〜〜〜〜〜✦

WHEN we talk to God in simple faith, we may be quite sure that He will answer our prayers.

And if we try to love Him, as we know that He loves us, we shall see all sorts of wonderful things happen. For love on the wings of prayer becomes the key to all the treasures of heaven.

Have you ever asked God for something that you really needed, or something that would bring happiness to others, and then watched for the answer? It's a lovely thing to do; and if you ask in faith, believing that God can and will do it for you, there will be no doubt about the result.

I am so sure about it because of the hundreds of times that children, and grownups too, have told me about the answers to prayer that they have had. Many of these have already appeared in "Bedtime Stories." Others are coming to me all the time.

Here is one that a little girl told me just the other day. It is very simple, but to that little girl it meant a great deal. She will never forget it.

I was attending a large camp meeting, telling stories to the children as usual. After one story hour a little girl came up to me and asked if she could tell me a story. I don't remember her name, but I do remember that she was wearing a pretty blue coat. Usually I don't remember clothes very well, but I do remember that blue coat.   And there's a reason.

"Mother bought me this coat," she said, "just before the camp meeting.   It cost more than seven dollars, which is a lot of money for us to pay.   Mother was so pleased with it.   But then, what do you suppose I did?   I lost it. Lost it!   I couldn't find it anywhere."

"What did mother say?" I asked.

"I didn't dare tell her," said the little girl.   "I was afraid."

"What did you do then?"

"Well, it so happened that just then I picked up a copy of 'Bedtime Stories' and began to read some of those wonderful answers to children's prayers.   And I said to myself, If Jesus answered those prayers, why shouldn't He answer mine?   And right then and there I got down on my knees and asked Him to help me find my coat before mother found out that I had lost it."

"Good girl," I said, smiling.   "But how did you find it?"

"Well, I kept on praying and searching.   I looked all over the campground.   Then I came into this building, and there on a chair, away off in a corner, I saw my coat. Was I happy?   I am sure it was an answer to my prayer; don't you think so, Uncle?"

"Of course," I said.   "I know it was."

God loves to help His children in all their worries and sorrows, whether they be small or large.

But here is another story, even more wonderful.

This is about a mother who had five children.   Her husband had been away from home for a long time, and no money had come from him for several weeks.   Every penny she had had was spent, and she was beginning to wonder what she would do for food, light, and heat for herself and her children during the long, cold winter days ahead.

Her biggest worry at the moment was the gas bill. It amounted to two dollars. She had received it weeks before, and today the "final notice" had come from the gas company, saying that the bill must be paid at once or they would cut off the gas.

Cut off the gas! Why, that would mean that there would be no way to cook the food or even boil a kettle of water. Feeling very much distressed, she decided to go for a walk, and, putting on her coat, she went down the street toward the little church which she attended.

A strong, cold wind was blowing, but she didn't seem to notice it. She could think of nothing but that gas bill, and now and then she would murmur a little prayer, "Dear Lord, please help me to pay it soon; don't let them cut off the gas."

Presently, for some reason, she stepped off the sidewalk and began to walk down the streetcar tracks. Then, all of a sudden, the high wind slapped something across her face. Her hand went up instantly, and she caught a piece of paper. It was a dollar bill! And before she could believe her eyes, lo, a second bill blew in her face, and she caught that one, too.

No more came. Just two.

"Thank you, Jesus," she whispered, as she went on down the street, smiling; "that's just what I needed."

Wonderful, isn't it, how some prayers are answered?

This time the answer came "on the wings of the wind."

H. A. Roberts

Prayer Time

Two Years After

WE must remember, of course, that all prayers are not answered immediately. Sometimes, for some good reason, God makes us wait, perhaps for a month, perhaps for a year, perhaps for even two years or more. But He never forgets a prayer. Just how He remembers them all, I don't know. But He does, and sometimes, long after we have forgotten that we asked for something, it comes along to remind us of His thoughtfulness and love.

So it was with a woman I heard about not long ago. Arriving home one day, she discovered, to her great distress, that she had lost her handbag.

This was no slight loss, for the bag contained more than fifty dollars in cash and a number of valuable papers.

Fifty dollars gone! It was terrible.

She telephoned to the police. She put an advertisement in the local newspaper, and when nothing happened, she put it in several other newspapers. She tried to think of every place she had been of late and then walked back over the same ground, searching carefully every step of the way. But no trace of the missing handbag could she find.

She prayed about it. Her husband prayed with her, yet nothing happened. They kept on praying for several weeks and then decided to let the matter drop.

Sometimes they said to each other, "Perhaps this is something too hard for the Lord." And maybe that is why He made them wait.

Several weeks later, around Christmas time, a young man was crossing a field in this same neighborhood, when, to his amazement, he saw a woman's handbag lying in the long grass. He picked it up and took it home, intending to telephone the police about it. But being very busy just then, he tossed the bag unopened into a closet and promptly forgot all about it.

Twelve months passed. Yes, twelve whole months. Believe it or not, it was Christmas the next year before that handbag was found again.

All this long time it had lain perfectly safe and undisturbed in its dark resting place.

Once more the young man went to the closet, and to his surprise saw a strange handbag there. He seemed to recall having picked it up somewhere, but he was not too sure about it. However, having some time on his hands now, he thought he would open it up and see what was inside.

Imagine his amazement when he found more than fifty dollars in cash!

At last he came across the owner's name and address, and a few minutes later he was hurrying over to apologize for having kept the bag so long.

And what do you suppose the woman said when at last the precious bag was in her hands once more, all safe and sound, with nothing missing, after having been lost for nearly two years? Well, I don't know what she said to the young man, but I am certain that when she said her prayers that night, she had something to say to God!

Which all goes to show that we should not give up hoping when our prayers are not answered just when we think they should be. God knows best; and it may be good for us, sometimes, to wait awhile.

Just in Time!

WHEN God sends us the help we need, He loves to send it just in time—not too soon, and not too late, but just when we need it most.

When the children of Israel were fleeing from the cruel Egyptians, they found themselves in a very difficult place. There were mountains on one side of them, the Red Sea in front of them, and the Egyptians behind them.

They were caught, and their plight could hardly have been worse. Nearer and nearer came the Egyptians. In fact, God let them come so close that His people could actually see them, and they were really frightened.

Another few hours and all would have been over. There would have been a dreadful slaughter, and those not killed would have been dragged back into slavery.

Just then, when hope of being saved had almost gone, God made a way through the sea. The Bible says: "Moses stretched out his hand over the sea; and the Lord caused the sea to go back by a strong east wind all that night, and made the sea dry land, and the waters were divided." Ex. 14:21.

The children of Israel walked through the sea to safety, just in time.

Another Bible story you know well is the one about the three young men who were thrown into the "burning fiery furnace," because they refused to worship the golden image set up by King Nebuchadnezzar.

The Children of Israel Leaving Egypt on Their Way to the Red Sea

Now a fiery furnace is a very hot place, but this furnace, we are told, was heated "seven times more than it was wont to be heated," and that must have been hot indeed.

But the Hebrew youth were not burned. In fact, we read that not even their hair was singed, nor did their clothes smell of smoke! Dan. 3:27.

How did this happen? Well, even while the big, burly soldiers were binding the young men, to throw them into the fire, the dear Lord Himself came to their rescue.

King Nebuchadnezzar, peering into the fiery furnace, beheld a sight that astonished him.

"Did not we cast three men bound into the midst of the fire?" he asked his counselors. They replied, "True, O king."

And the king exclaimed: "Lo, I see four men loose, walking in the midst of the fire, and they have no hurt; and the form of the fourth is like the Son of God." Dan. 3:25.

Again God had come to the rescue, just in time.

The same thing happened when Daniel himself got into trouble. You remember how some wicked people tried to stop his praying to God, and how, because he refused, he was thrown into a den of lions.

Well, everybody else who had ever been thrown to those lions had been torn to pieces in a minute, but when Daniel entered the den, the lions behaved like tame pussy-cats! They walked around him and smelled him, but they never touched him.

When the king came to the den in the morning to find out what had happened, he called out: "O Daniel, servant of the living God, is thy God, whom thou servest continually, able to deliver thee from the lions?" Dan. 6:20.

Whether or not he expected to hear an answering voice out of the den we cannot tell, but to his delight there came a reply in strong, happy tones: "O king, live forever. My God hath sent His angel, and hath shut the lions' mouths, that they have not hurt me." Verses 21, 22.

I wonder when that angel was sent. Perhaps just as the order was given for Daniel to be cast to the lions, or perhaps when the soldiers were dragging Daniel out of his house to take him to the den. I don't know; but I do like to think that another order was given at the same time by another King, an order to the swiftest angel in heaven to fly with all speed to the rescue of this faithful child of God. And he arrived, just in time.

When Jesus came to live on this earth for a little while, He was always arriving just in time to help people. Sometimes the people who wanted His help thought He came too late, but He always proved that the time was just right.

Maybe you remember the wonderful story of Lazarus. This poor man became very sick, and his two sisters, Mary and Martha, immediately thought of Jesus and how He had healed so many other sick people. As they were very friendly with Jesus, they felt sure He would come soon and make their brother well. But He didn't come. Though He knew all about what was happening, He did not hurry at all, and finally Lazarus died. Not till then did Jesus go to the home. As He arrived He was met by Martha, who said: "Lord, if Thou hadst been here, my brother had not died." John 11:21.

Martha was really rebuking Jesus for having come too late. But it is never too late for the Lord. Always when He seems to delay things a little, He has some beautiful purpose in it, and this time it was to raise Lazarus from the dead. So His seeming lateness led to the most wonderful miracle He ever performed. So, after all, He was really just in time again.

Because He never changes, He is ready to be as thoughtful for us and our needs today as ever He was for His people in the olden days. As He helped them, so He will help us, just in time.

I remember so well having to move to a new place of work some years ago. It meant leaving the house in which I had lived for several years, and I tried my best to

Daniel in the Lions' Den
Britton Riviere, Artist

dispose of it. But I couldn't sell it, and I couldn't rent it; so finally I had to leave it empty—with the Lord. Months and months passed, and still the house stood unoccupied. Meanwhile I lived in all sorts of uncomfortable places, looking for a new house, but unable to get one because the first was not sold. Then one day I found the very house I thought I needed. It seemed to fit every purpose, and I had just a few hours in which to buy it. Before those hours had passed I received a telegram saying, "House sold."

I shall never forget that moment, for it was very wonderful to me.

I said, "Thank you, Lord. Just in time again!"

And here is a lovely story that someone sent me the

other day. It is about a mother, her five-year-old daughter, and their old, old car.

Exactly how old their car is, I wouldn't like to say, but I know it has seen thirteen summers at least, which makes it pretty old as cars go nowadays.

Well, one day this mother and her little girl set out in their car to go to visit some neighbors. They were going to do some missionary work, I believe.

They were out and about for a good long time, and finally turned toward home. Bravely the old car chugged along until it came to the center of an important intersection. There it stopped and positively refused to move another inch.

Fortunately, they were out in the country, and there was no traffic in sight at the moment; so there was no immediate cause for alarm. But it was bothersome just the same, especially when they were both very tired.

Mother wondered what to do for the best. She looked at the gas. There was plenty. She looked at everything else she could think of that might be wrong, but all seemed in order.

Again and again she pressed her foot on the starter, but nothing happened. The old car just wouldn't go. Perhaps it was tired, too!

Five minutes passed. Ten minutes. Fifteen minutes. Twenty minutes. Fancy being stalled in the middle of an intersection for twenty minutes! But still the car wouldn't move an inch, and mother began to get very nervous and upset.

Just then they heard a noise in the distance, and, looking up, saw a great big oil truck coming down the road toward them at a great pace.

There was no room for it to pass, and if it should try to go around, it would certainly get stuck in the mud and possibly overturn.

Mother wondered whether she should jump out of the car and run for safety; but she was so frightened she couldn't move, and there was her little girl to think of, too.

On and on came the truck, nearer and nearer. It seemed that in just a few seconds it must hit them.

And then, believe it or not, the little girl suddenly spoke and said, "Mother, why don't you ask Jesus to help us?"

The rebuke struck home like an arrow to the mother's heart. She bowed her head. The little girl did the same. They said the shortest little prayer they knew, "Jesus, please help us."

That was all, and it took just a moment.

Then mother pressed her foot on that starter again. There was a purring sound. The engine had started! A second more and the old car leaped forward, while the truck roared past behind them.

The old car chugged home at fifteen miles an hour and then stopped at their door. It never moved again until a great sum of money had been spent to renew the engine.

Of course, some people will say they know how it all happened, that it was just a lucky accident. But that dear mother has no doubt at all that it was an answer to their prayer. In fact, in her letter to me she said, "It was my little girl's faith that did it."

It was. And I like to think that this was but another of those wonderful occasions when God sends needed help "just in time."

The Faith Chickens Go for a Walk

The Faith Chickens

WHILE we are still thinking about wonderful answers to prayer, I must tell you this interesting story that someone sent to me a little while ago. It is absolutely true—like all the others, of course—and the only thing I am going to alter is the little boy's name. That is so you won't find out who the story is about.

Let's call him Richard. That's a good name, and I don't think he will be disappointed when he sees it.

Now Richard was eleven years old when this happened. He was just at the age when all boys like to have pets of one kind or another, and Richard had chosen chickens.

This was natural, for father had chickens, too, and Richard had helped to feed them and pick up the eggs.

Now, however, he wanted to have some of his very own. So, out of his own pocket money, he bought a sitting of eggs—thirteen—and put them under what he thought was a motherly old hen.

Now, you know as well as I do that it takes just three weeks to hatch chicken eggs, and no matter how anxious Richard was to get his first baby chicks, he had to wait just that long.

One week went by—two weeks.

Then something happened. That naughty mother hen walked off the eggs and refused to go back!

Richard coaxed and coaxed, but she refused to sit again.

As often as he put her back on the eggs, just so often would she walk off.

All this time the eggs were getting colder and colder, and, of course, if eggs get too cold, they will not hatch.

Richard ran across to a neighbor's house and begged for the loan of a sitting hen, for just one week, but they did not have one. He came back crying. The eggs were so cold now that the situation seemed hopeless.

Mother suggested that he look for a sitting hen in their own chicken house, and to his joy he found one there. In high spirits he carried the hen over to the coop and set her on the cold eggs.

Not wanting Richard to be too disappointed, mother warned him that there wasn't a chance that the eggs would hatch. "Why, dear," she said, "that bad old hen has been off them for a night and a day. I think you'll have to plan to try again sometime."

"Mother," said Richard, "I may have lost most of them, but I am sure I haven't lost them all."

"Why are you so sure, dear?" asked mother.

"Because I have asked Jesus to give me just one, and I believe He will."

"I hope so," said mother cautiously, "but I am afraid it is expecting too much."

The last week passed. Even the last day.

The eggs were as solid as ever. There wasn't a sign of a chick anywhere.

That was a Sunday morning, and mother, disappointed herself, turned to Richard and said, "How is your faith now?"

Very seriously Richard looked at mother and said, "What's the matter with tomorrow?"

Monday came, but no chicks.

Tuesday came, and no chicks.

Wednesday morning came, and still no chicks.

There was no use hoping any longer, thought mother, and when Richard came home from school in the afternoon, she told him to break the eggs and not keep the poor old hen in the stuffy coop any longer.

Sadly Richard went over to the coop to say good-by to his last hope. Then suddenly he came rushing back to the house.

"Mother!" he nearly shrieked. "Mother! Come! Come quickly! I can hear something saying, 'Peep.' I am sure I have a chick."

Mother ran as she hadn't run anywhere for some time, and sure enough, under the hen they found the prettiest, fluffiest little baby chick they had ever seen.

"Aha!" cried Richard. "So God has answered my prayer after all!"

He had indeed, and, as He so often does, He answered it in double measure, "pressed down, . . . and running over;" for the next day, Thursday, another little chick, a black fellow this time, was hatched, four days late.

That made only two out of the whole thirteen, but, oh, how precious were those two from that day on!

Richard said he believed God had been testing his faith by making him wait so long.

And that is how these two little birds came to be called "the faith chickens."

This Boy Has Three Dogs to Look After Him!

Good Old Rover

~~~~~~~~~~~~~~~~~~~~~~~~~

DO you happen to have a dog that loves you? If so, you are very fortunate. Look after him well, for you never know when he may do you some great kindness.

Rover was a dog like this, faithful and true. He watched over little Freddie with the tenderest care. In fact, Freddie's big sister Sylvia used to wonder if there was anything Rover would not try to do for the boy.

One day she found out that there was indeed no limit to his love.

Freddie was riding around the house on his scooter, with Rover chasing after him. They were having the happiest time together, and Freddie's shrieks of delight were mingled with Rover's cheerful barking. Looking out of an upstairs window, Sylvia thought it was one of the prettiest sights she had ever seen.

Then suddenly everything went wrong, and Sylvia was struck dumb with fright.

Running into a brick that had been carelessly left on the driveway, Freddie fell off his scooter with a terrible crash and lay half-stunned on the ground. This was bad enough, but coming straight toward him at this moment was a heavy truck, which was being backed out of the garage by father himself!

So frightened was Sylvia that she couldn't say a word. She wanted to bang on the window, but she couldn't move. All she could do was to watch and wait for the worst.

Then she saw something wonderful happen. Like a flash of lightning Rover leaped on top of the prostrate form of his little master and, glaring furiously at the approaching truck, barked as he had never barked before.

Nearer and nearer came the truck, for of course father could not see what was lying on the road behind him.

Nearer and nearer! but still Rover stood there barking and barking—short, sharp barks in rapid succession, as though crying, Stop! Stop! Stop!

An inch or two away from Freddie's head the truck stopped, and father jumped out.

"What's all this noise about, Rover?" he cried.

Then he saw everything.

Do you wonder that they made a big fuss over Rover that night?

H. A. Roberts

Patching Up the House

✦ ⌁⌁⌁⌁⌁⌁⌁⌁⌁⌁⌁⌁⌁⌁⌁⌁⌁⌁⌁ ✦

G ERALD had just completed his list of new-year
resolutions.

Just why he had made the list he was not quite sure,
but the most important reason, no doubt, was that the
boy next door had just done the same. It was the thing
to do.

Gerald looked down his list and began to wonder how
long he would keep some of his promises.

For instance, the list began: "I resolve that I will always get up early in the morning."

"That," he said to himself, "will probably last about a
week at the most."

Then there was, "I resolve that I will not tease my baby
sister."

"That one," he told himself, "will hardly last out the
afternoon."

Next came, "I resolve to help mother wash the dishes
once a day without grumbling."

"A good resolution," he thought, "but not likely to
be kept after school starts."

Next, "I resolve never to read any book or paper that
mother doesn't approve."

Gerald wasn't too sure about this one, and he wondered
what he should do with the comics he had hidden at the
bottom of his bureau drawer.

Next, "I resolve that I will never again say a bad word."

"Now I'll be—" began Gerald, pulling himself up short; "why did I make this resolution?"

Just then mother came in, and, seeing Gerald so interested, asked if she might read what was written on the piece of paper he held in his hand.

Mother smiled and said she was pleased that Gerald was "turning over a new leaf" and planning to be such a good boy.

"But I wonder how long they will last?" she said with a smile.

"Oh, not long, I suppose," said Gerald, laughing. "But there, it was fun to make up the list. All the boys around here are doing it."

"I suppose it is a good idea to make these resolutions," said mother, "but I never had much faith in them."

"Why not?" asked Gerald.

"Oh, well," began mother, "just because they are so seldom kept. To my mind it is like patching up an old house."

"Patching up a house, mother!" laughed Gerald. "What makes you say that?"

"Well, I would have to tell you a story to explain exactly what I mean."

"Go on, tell it," urged Gerald, who loved stories above everything else.

"Long, long ago," began mother, "there was a family living in one of the Eastern States. Deciding, as many other people had, to go west, they packed everything into their covered wagon and started off. After traveling a few hundred miles they stopped, built a house, and settled down. But the oldest boy was not satisfied. He wanted to go farther west still; so, bidding the family good-by, he moved on. Week after week he trudged westward, coming finally to a tract of land that really appealed to him. It was very fertile, and had plenty of water. Here he built a small shack for himself and started farming on his own.

"Years passed by. Other people came to the same district. Soon a village sprang up. Then it grew to be a small town, and then a city.

"Still this boy, now grown to be an old man, dwelt in his humble little shack. He liked it. Other people could have mansions if they wanted them, but, 'Give me my little shack,' said he. However, the people around didn't like having that little old shack in the midst of their beautiful homes. They said it spoiled the whole district, and should be torn down. Some of them tried to buy the place, but the old man steadfastly refused to sell.

"At last one day two well-dressed men called at the little shack. The old man invited them in and asked them what they wanted.

" 'We have come to buy your shack,' they said.

" 'Nothing doing,' said the old man. 'I've lived here many years, and I'm going to live here till I die.'

" 'But we are willing to pay you a very big price,' they said. 'See, here is a check for $100,000. If you will just sign this receipt, the cash is yours.'

"The old man had never seen so much money before in all his life. This was more than all he had ever earned put together. Perhaps, he thought, such a chance to make a lot of money would never come his way again.

"He signed, and the men went away, promising to return in a day or two with the final documents.

"Hardly had they left, however, before his conscience pricked him. He told himself that he should not have taken so much money for the place. It was a swindle. Why, it wasn't worth a thousand dollars, let alone a hundred thousand. Look at that door half off its hinges, and that window that wouldn't close, and the chimney that smoked so badly.

" 'Well,' he thought to himself, 'if I am going to take so much money for it, at least I ought to patch it up a bit.' So he took off his coat and went at the job. Some things he could mend, and some he couldn't, but at least he tried hard to make a good show.

"By and by the two men returned, and the final documents were signed. As they were leaving, the old man

H. Hofmann, Artist

Jesus Wanted to Make This Young Man's Life Great and Beautiful, but the Youth Wanted to Patch Up the Old Shack He Had Built Himself

spoke up. 'I hope,' he said, 'you have noticed what I have done to the place since you were here the last time.'

" 'Done to it?' they asked. 'What have you done to it? Oh, you shouldn't have bothered. We are going to tear it all down and build a mansion here.'

"And so it is," concluded mother, "with us and our resolutions."

"But I don't quite see what you mean," began Gerald.

"I know," said mother, "but it is this way: We keep trying and trying to patch up all that is wrong about us by saying, 'I resolve this,' and, 'I resolve that,' but it doesn't do any good. You see, Gerald, Jesus has bought the whole property—every bit of us—and He wants to build a beautiful mansion in place of our little shack. All we have to do is to ask Him to come into our hearts. Then He will get to work and change everything Himself. He will even change our desires, so that we will not want to do wrong things or say wrong words or even hide silly comics in a drawer, so that mother won't see them."

At this revelation of the completeness of mother's knowledge of his doings, Gerald blushed all over his face and down his back.

"Er—er—er," he began, "er—er—excuse me, mother, just a minute. There's something I want to do."

For a moment mother wondered what it could be that Gerald had so suddenly thought about; but as she listened she could hear a drawer being pulled out of a bureau and something being stuffed into a wastepaper basket.

The new mansion was being built already!

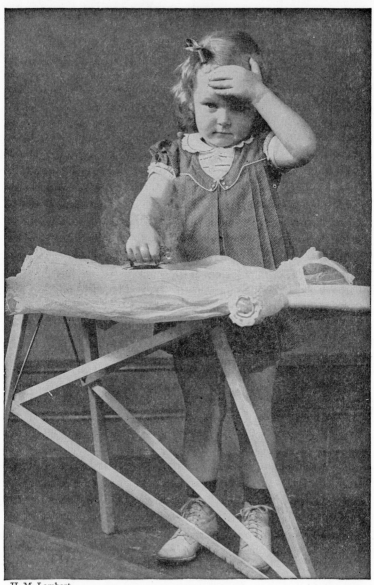

H. M. Lambert

Iris Tries to Help Mother

Iris Does the Ironing

✦﹌﹌﹌﹌﹌﹌﹌﹌﹌﹌﹌﹌﹌﹌﹌✦

"IRIS, dear," said mother, "I am going out for a little while, and I want you to be a very good girl till I come back."

"All right, mamma," said Iris, who didn't mind being left alone, provided mother didn't stay away too long.

"I am just going to do a little shopping," said mother; "and if you are *very* good, I'll bring you something nice."

"Ooh!" cried Iris. "I'll be good, mamma. Bring me some candy. A nice lot."

"I will," said mother; "but now, Iris, you won't touch anything you shouldn't, will you?"

"Oh, no, no, no!" said Iris, with great assurance, and looking so good that one would think she had never done anything wrong in all her little life.

"And mind, darling, you won't touch the iron, will you? It might give you a bad burn."

"Oh, no, no, no!" murmured Iris. "I'm going to play with my dollies until you come back."

"Well, then, give me a kiss," said mother, and away she went.

As soon as mother had gone, Iris started to have fun with her dolls; but after she had tucked them both up in their carriage and told them to go to sleep, she began to look around for something else to do. Then she got a bright idea.

"I think I'll do something to help mamma," she said to

herself, "and give her a big surprise when she comes home."

So Iris wandered around the house, looking for a job she could do that would please mother.

"Maybe," she thought, "I could wash a few dishes;" but no, they were all washed.

"Perhaps I could do some dusting," she told herself; but again mamma had done it all. Everywhere Iris went, the place was perfectly clean and tidy.

Finally she came back into the kitchen, and her eyes caught sight of a basket half full of clothes waiting to be ironed.

"There's an idea!" Iris thought to herself. "I could do the ironing for mamma. And won't she be surprised?"

So she found the ironing board and managed to open it up just as she had seen her mother do. Then she found the iron and put the plug in its socket.

Once she remembered that mother had said something about not touching the iron, but she thought that mother wouldn't mind so long as she was helping her.

"After all," she said to herself, "mamma just didn't want me to burn myself, and of course I wouldn't do that. Ironing is a pleasant thing to do. Mamma's lucky to be able to do it every week."

Hearing a crackling sound in the iron, Iris decided that it must be getting warm. It was. Then she remembered that mother always tested the iron to make sure whether it was the right temperature; so she tried it the same way.

"It must be hot enough now," she said to herself. Then, picking up a few of her own little handkerchiefs, she spread them out carefully, and gently moved the iron up and down over them.

"It's easy," she said, "easy. I just love ironing."

One by one she finished the handkerchiefs, and then picked up a garment of mother's.

"I think I had better sprinkle this," she said, and proceeded to get a bowl of water, leaving the iron on the ironing board as she went over to the faucet.

Returning with the water, she sprinkled some over the garment, and then she started to pick up the iron. A strange smell was coming from under it, but she did not worry very much. She thought she had smelled something like this once or twice when mother was ironing; so probably it was all right.

This garment of mother's, however, was a little more difficult than the flat handkerchiefs. It wouldn't go straight. So she pressed a little harder, and that made a brown mark, and when she pressed again, it became a darker brown still. Finally, when there were a number of brown marks all over it, she thought she had better put it down and try something else.

"Oh," she said, "there's my own bestest party frock. I didn't know that mother had washed it. Won't it be fun to iron that!"

So she picked up the frock, spread it out, and sprinkled it all over with water.

Then she picked up the iron again. It seemed to have got a bit hotter by now, and there was another of those brown marks where it had been sitting on the board—a dark-brown one, in fact. She thought mother might not be pleased about it. But there was her dress to iron; she must get on with that.

This proved to be even more difficult than mother's garment. It was of a thin material, and just wouldn't lie straight. And every time the iron went down on the wet spots a cloud of steam would rise in the air all around her face. At least, it started as steam, but it smelled a little like smoke after a while.

Just then there was a click of a key in the front door, and Iris dropped the iron and ran to where she had been playing with her dolls. Unfortunately, in her haste, she forgot to pull out the plug.

A moment later mother was rushing into the kitchen. A strange blue cloud was rising from the ironing board.

"Iris! You naughty girl!" she cried. "What have you been doing? Why, look at your best party dress! It's ruined. It's burned clear through. Oh, and look at my—!" But mother couldn't finish. She was too upset.

"I was only trying to help you," said Iris, holding one of her dollies very tightly.

"Help me!" cried mother. "It is much better to obey than to help in this manner."

"Did you bring me any candy?" asked Iris, trying to change the subject.

"There'll be no candy for you, my dear, for a long time to come," said mother firmly.

And then mother walked upstairs with Iris's hand tightly clasped in hers.

Just what was going to happen up there I am not quite sure. Perhaps you can guess.

The Last Marshmallow

I T was dinnertime, and the whole family was sitting around the dining table, enjoying a good meal. There were father and mother and Big Sister and Big Brother and Little Brother and Baby Brother, and they were all having a very happy time together.

In the center of the table was a little blue-and-white box. Mother had placed it there for a very special treat, and every now and then the children's eyes would turn toward it eagerly.

They all knew what was inside it, for, of course, it was a marshmallow box; and as they all liked marshmallows very much, they could hardly wait for mother to open it.

The soup and the potatoes, the cabbage and the carrots, the milk and the rice pudding, were all hurried on their way because of the thought that there were to be marshmallows to finish off the meal.

And then, when all the food was gone, and all the dishes had been removed from the table, something unlooked for happened! Mother went to open the box and found that it was empty! That is, it was empty save for one little marshmallow sitting lonesomely in a corner.

Everyone's face dropped. You couldn't imagine a sadder family.

"Why, look at that!" exclaimed mother. "I thought the box was full. Now isn't that disappointing!"

"But who could have eaten them all?" asked Big Sister.

"Oh, I remember now," said mother. "I must have opened the box when the visitors came the other day, and I never thought another thing about it. I am sorry. What shall we do?"

"There's not much we can do," said father, "except cut the one that's left into six pieces."

Everyone laughed.

"What's the use of doing that?" asked Big Brother. "You wouldn't even be able to taste it."

"Well," said Big Sister, "I think it would be much better to let someone have the marshmallow whole, and then we shall all enjoy watching him eat it."

"That's a good idea," said father; "but who is to have it?"

"I want it," cried Baby Brother, who had been watching with deep interest all that had been going on. "Give it to me."

"We'll see," said father.

"I'm going to have it!" cried Baby Brother, reaching out his little arm to grab box, marshmallow, and all.

"Here, not so fast," said Big Brother, catching the arm just in time. "We haven't decided yet."

"But I want it!" screamed Baby Brother. "Let me go! I'm going to have it. It's mine."

"Just a minute, now, sonny boy," said father. "I think we should put this to the vote. There's only one marshmallow; so, clearly, we can't all eat it. I'm going to find out what everyone thinks about this. I'll start here on my right. Now, Big Sister, when there is only one marshmallow in the house, who should have it?"

"Mother, of course," said Big Sister.

"All right. Now, Big Brother, when there is only

one marshmallow in the house, who should have it?"

"Mother, of course," said Big Brother.

"Very good. We all seem to be thinking alike. Now, Little Brother, when there is only one marshmallow in the house, who should have it?"

"Mother, of course," said Little Brother.

Everyone laughed again.

"Well, that's fine," said father. "Now we come to you, sonny boy. I am going to ask you the same question, and I want you to think very hard before you answer it. Now, when there is only one marshmallow in the house, who should eat it?"

"Me!" cried Baby Brother, making another grab at the box.

"Steady now," said Big Brother, grabbing the little arm again. "I didn't think you could be so selfish."

"I'm not selfish!" cried Baby Brother. "I want that marshmallow. It's mine! It's mine."

"Well," said father, "I'm afraid there's no other way, mother, except for you to eat that marshmallow. The vote is three to one in your favor. And now I'm adding my vote, too; so that makes four to one, which is a good majority. Pass mother the marshmallow!"

Now mother didn't really want to eat that marshmallow. She had something else in mind. So, turning to Baby Brother, she said: "Now, darling, just once more. If there were only one marshmallow left in all the wide, wide world, who should have it?"

"Me!" roared Baby Brother.

"Too bad," said mother; "I suppose I shall have to eat it after all."

And she did.

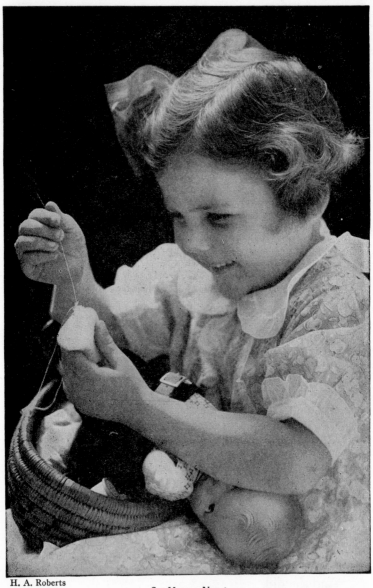

H. A. Roberts

So Happy Now!

Helen's Way to Happiness

L ITTLE Helen was wandering through the house, looking as sad as if she had broken all her dolls and lost all her money at the same time.

"What is the matter with you, Helen?" asked mother. "You look so miserable."

"I am miserable," said Helen, bursting into tears.

"Oh, darling, what can have gone wrong with my little girl?" mother asked tenderly.

"Oh, dear," sobbed Helen, "there's nobody to play with, and nothing to do, and nowhere to go. I'm just, oh, so miserable!" And Helen sobbed louder than ever.

"You poor little thing," said mother. "Let me see, what can we do about it?"

"There's nothing to do about it," wailed Helen.

"But, darling," suggested mother, trying to wipe the tears away, "why don't you go and play with the little girl next door?"

"She doesn't want to play with me."

"Doesn't want to play with you! Why not?"

"She's going out with her mamma, and she'd rather go out with her mamma than play with me."

"I see," said mother. "Well, then, why don't you look at your picture books?"

"Don't want to look at my picture books."

"Well, then, why don't you—let me see—or—why

don't you go and look at your garden and see how everything is growing after the rain?"

"I don't want to go and look at my garden," said Helen, wiping a tiny handkerchief over her eyes.

Suddenly mother had a bright idea.

"I have it!" she cried.

"What do you have?" asked Helen, mildly interested.

"I know just what is the matter with you," said mother. "Really, I believe I do."

"There's nothing the matter with me," said Helen. "I just want somebody to play with me."

"Yes, I think I do know," said mother. "There's something the matter right inside you."

"Where?"

"Oh, somewhere inside," smiled mother.

"What is it?"

"Just a little teeny-weeny thought that isn't quite right."

"What isn't quite right? I only want somebody to play with me."

"I know," said mother. "But, darling, I believe that if you stopped thinking about yourself just for a minute or two, and began to think about somebody else, then you would be happy again right away."

This was a new idea for Helen, and as she hadn't anything to say about it, mother went on.

"Don't you think it would be a good idea to plan something pleasant for somebody else, perhaps a surprise of some kind?"

"I don't know anyone to surprise," said Helen.

"Oh, darling, of course you do," said mother. "Don't you remember that sick little girl we went to visit in the hospital one day? You know, the one who can't walk.

And you said that you were so sorry for her that you would fix up one of your own dollies and take it to her to make her happy. But I'm afraid you forgot all about it."

"Oh, yes, I did forget all about it!" said Helen, her face very thoughtful for a moment. "And I told her that I was going to bring it to her! Oh, dear, what will she think of me?"

"Well, darling, why don't you find that dolly right now and start getting it ready? Then perhaps tomorrow we shall take it down to the hospital."

"All right, mamma," said Helen, her face brightening up. "Shall I wash the dolly's clothes?"

"Surely," said mother; "you couldn't give away a dolly with dirty clothes on, could you?"

"No," laughed Helen. "And shall I fix her socks? One of them has a hole in it."

"You can try," said mother. "And if you can't manage it, then I'll help you."

"And, mother," said Helen, all interested now, "will you find an attractive box to pack it in, and some tissue paper, and some ribbon to tie round the box, so it will look like a real present?"

"I will," said mother as Helen ran upstairs to find the dolly. Soon she was down again and busy as a little bee.

By and by mother heard a chuckle coming from the next room. She looked round the door, and there was Helen, sitting on a little chair, doing her best to mend the dolly's socks.

"I'm having such fun," said Helen, tears and loneliness all forgotten now.

"I'm so glad," said mother; "and you know, dear, it always is fun to do something to make someone else happy."

The More Jennie Whispered the More Jessie Laughed

The Twins' Secret

JENNIE and Jessie loved secrets. If Jennie wasn't telling one to Jessie, then Jessie was telling one to Jennie. So there was always a secret going on somewhere, somehow.

Now one fine morning Jessie came up very close to Jennie's ear and whispered that she had another secret to tell.

"What is it?" asked Jennie.

"Promise you won't tell?"

"Of course I won't tell," said Jessie. "Go on."

Jennie came closer still and put her hands up beside her mouth so that nobody should hear. Then she whispered and whispered and whispered. And the more she whispered the more Jessie laughed, such a happy laugh that it brought mother into the room to find out what was going on.

"Another secret!" she said. "What is it all about this time?"

"Aaaaaaaah!" said the twins together. "We couldn't tell."

"Oh, but you were laughing so, it must have been a very special secret. Do tell your own mamma."

"We couldn't," said Jessie, "'cause it's all about you."

"Ssh!" whispered Jennie. "You're telling."

"About me!" exclaimed mother. "What secret do you have about me?"

"We couldn't tell you," said Jennie. "But it's about your headache."

73

"Now *you're* telling!" whispered Jessie.

"About my headache!" said mother. "What are you planning about my headache?"

"Oh, we couldn't tell you," said Jessie, "'cause it's an extra-special secret. But we are going to let you stay in bed—"

"Sssssh! *You're* telling now!" whispered Jennie.

"Let me stay in bed!" said mother; "and what then?"

"Really we musn't tell you," said Jennie. "It would just spoil everything. But when we keep you in bed, Jessie and I are going to do all the work—"

"Sssssh! *You're* telling it all now," whispered Jessie.

"Going to do all the work!" exclaimed mother. "How lovely—"

"Yes, mamma," burst in Jennie. "Of course, you mustn't know anything about it, but tomorrow we are going to bring your breakfast upstairs to bed—"

"Yes, mamma," cried Jessie, "and we are going to wash all the dishes and sweep all the floors—"

"And dust all the furniture," put in Jennie.

"And we won't make the least little bit of noise—" said Jessie.

"So you can sleep a long, long time," added Jennie.

"And get better," said Jessie.

Suddenly Jennie turned to Jessie. "You're telling the secret."

"No, you are."

"I'm not; you are."

"It's all right, darlings," broke in mother, laughing. "Nobody has really told me very much, has she? And it's one of the best secrets I ever heard about in all my life!"

The Boy Who Was
Always Best

✣ ⌇⌇⌇⌇⌇⌇⌇⌇⌇⌇⌇⌇⌇⌇⌇⌇⌇⌇⌇⌇⌇⌇⌇⌇⌇⌇⌇⌇⌇⌇ ✣

ALBERT had a very strange idea in his little head.
He was quite sure that everything he did and everything he said was "best."

Even when he was a very tiny boy he said to his mother,
"Don't you think my teeth are sharper than anybody else's
teeth?" And another time he said, "Mamma, I can eat
faster than all the other boys in the world, can't I?"

When he was older he said, "Can't I ride fast on my
bicycle!—faster than anybody else; don't you think so,
mamma?"

And he was always sure that he could build better
houses with his bricks than anybody had ever built before.

Once he even said that he was sure his dog was prettier
than all the other dogs in the world, which made everybody
laugh.

Of course it was all very funny in a way, and yet it was
something that Albert's mother didn't like very well. Nobody really wants to hear someone praise himself all the
time, and the sooner little boys—and little girls, too—learn
that lesson, the better for them. At least, that is what
Albert's mother thought, and she tried to think of some
way to help her little boy understand.

So one day she told Albert that she was going to have

a party especially for him, and that she would invite two or three boys he had never met before.

Albert was delighted, and looked forward eagerly to the promised day.

"Mamma," he said, "I guess mine is going to be the best party that anybody ever had."

"I believe it will be," said mother, with a twinkle in her eye.

At last the great day arrived, and right on time there came to the house three of the pleasantest little boys Albert had ever seen.   They were so kind and friendly that he wished they would stay and play with him always.

Mother had arranged quite a full program of games and races, and soon there was plenty of noise and laughter around the house and the garden.

After a while mother noticed that Albert was beginning to get a strange look on his face, as though he wasn't too well pleased about something.   But she didn't say anything.

By and by she planned a running race through the orchard to a big apple tree and back.   Away they all went, and Albert ran his very hardest, but still he came in last.

The same thing happened when it came to racing on his little bicycle, with mother taking the time with her watch. Sometimes Albert would come in second or third, but he just couldn't get to be first.

When it was time to come indoors, they all played with Albert's bricks, and Jerry, one of the visitors, built such a beautiful castle that even Albert had to admit that it was better than his.

When mealtime came, Albert seemed to try to make up for being behind in so many other things by eating the cake so fast that mother had to tell him to be careful, or he would choke himself.

Finally the time came for the visitors to leave, and when they had gone, mother asked Albert how he had enjoyed the party.

"Oh, fairly well," he said.

"You weren't really happy, were you?" said mother.

"How did you know?" asked Albert.

"I could see it in your face," said mother; "and I think I know what was the matter."

"There wasn't anything the matter," said Albert.

"I think there was," said mother. "You didn't like to have those other little boys winning the races and doing other things better than you did."

Albert was silent, and mother knew that she had touched the spot.

"Why, darling, the only time when you were quicker than the others was when you gobbled up the cake, and that wasn't a very polite thing to do."

Albert blushed, and mother said nothing for a moment or two.

"You know, darling," she said, "no one can be best in everything. I can't. You can't. It wouldn't be good for us. And if we expect always to be first and best, we shall never be really happy, for we shall keep on seeing somebody getting ahead of us. Of course, we may be best in some things, but we should ever be ready to agree that other people can be best in other things. Do you see what I mean?"

"Um," said Albert, and mother couldn't tell whether it meant yes or no, but at least she did not hear so much about his being best after that.

Galloway

Busy Boys Are Happy Boys

God's Busy Men

"OH, dear me!" sighed Maurice, as he stretched his arms and legs and then turned over for another snooze on the sofa. "This suits me better than work."

He gave another comfortable little grunt and quickly went off to sleep again.

How long he would have slept if something hadn't happened to wake him up, I don't know. But something did happen, quite soon.

Father turned up.

"Where's that lazy, good-for-nothing boy?" he was saying to himself as he came through the door. "I left him to do that job, and he has run off again. Wait until I get hold of him! Hello! Well, of all things!"

He had caught sight of Maurice fast asleep on the sofa.

"Hi! Wake up there!" cried father, pulling Maurice's legs onto the floor.

Maurice opened his eyes and frowned, but seeing who had wakened him, he jumped to his feet.

"What are you doing here?" asked father. "Why aren't you out helping the other boys stack that wood?"

"Just didn't feel like it," said Maurice.

"Didn't feel like it!" said father. "Supposing we all 'didn't feel like it' when there was work to be done? Come along now, and no more slacking."

Just then there was a sound of happy laughter as Jim and Wilfred burst into the room.

"Say, dad," they cried, "may we work in your old shed? We want to make something."

"Well, what about that wood you were going to stack for me this afternoon?"

"It's all done," they cried. "That is, we've done all you asked us to do. We left a bit for Maurice, of course."

"Finished already!" exclaimed father. "I don't know how you did it all so quickly. Well done! Of course you may work in my old shed. What do you want to make there?"

"One of those soap-box coasters, dad," said Wilfred. "We have the wheels already, and if we may work in your shed awhile, we'll soon have it finished."

"All right, go ahead," said father; and away went the two boys with shouts of delight.

"I suppose I had better go and move that wood," said Maurice.

"I suppose you had," said father; "and don't be long about it. Look at those other two boys. They have their part of the job all done, and now they're free to do something for themselves. How much better to do things that way! And they are always busy at something. No one ever sees them lolling around as you do."

"I think I'll be going," said Maurice, moving toward the door.

"Not for a moment," said father. "I have something I want to say to you."

"All right," said Maurice, turning back and then leaning against the wall.

"Now look at you," said father. "Can't even stand upright. Really, Maurice, you'll never get anywhere in life if you don't change your ways. You can't loaf along like this and expect to win. And what's more, son, when God looks for someone to do something big for Him, He never picks a lazy man."

Maurice flopped into a chair.

"It's a fact, son," went on father. "God chooses busy men. When He wanted someone to be His champion before the king of Egypt and bring the Israelites out of bondage, He found Moses caring for the sheep at Horeb.

"When He wanted a man to be the first king of Israel, He found Saul searching for his father's lost asses.

"When He wanted a man to contend with Goliath, He found David looking after his father's sheep and bravely fighting off the lions and the bears.

"When He wanted another champion to save His people from the Philistines, He found Gideon threshing wheat by the wine press.

"When He wanted a prophet to take Elijah's place, He found Elisha plowing with twelve yoke of oxen.

"When, later on, He wanted another man to be His prophet, He found Amos busy as a herdsman.

"When He wanted disciples to follow Him, and become the first leaders of His church, He found Peter and Andrew casting their net into the sea. Soon after He found James and John mending their nets. And not long after that He found Matthew busy at the tax office.

"It has always been that way, Maurice. When He wanted a man to start His missions in India, He found William Carey mending shoes.

"When He wanted someone to open up Africa to missions, He found Livingstone working beside a cotton machine.

"Yes, Maurice, always remember that God chooses

busy men. He never takes a lazy one for any big job He wants to get done."

Maurice stood up. "I suppose I'd better get on with that job now," he said.

"A good idea," said father; "now see how quickly you can get it done."

Maurice went out to the pile of wood and was soon at work.

Every now and then he would hear happy voices coming from father's old workshop, and he would wish that he had done his job earlier instead of lazing around on the sofa.

And all the time he was moving the chunks of wood one little sentence kept running through his mind. He simply couldn't forget it. It seemed as though someone was whispering it in his ear over and over again:

"God chooses busy men; God chooses busy men."

Slowly but surely a thought grew in his mind, and by and by he was saying to himself, "I want to be one of God's busy men, too."

How Billy Got Big
and Strong

✦〜〜〜〜〜〜〜〜〜〜〜〜〜〜〜〜〜〜〜〜✦

BILLY was a small boy for his age, and if there was one thing he wanted more than anything else in the world, it was to grow "big and strong."

At school he was about the smallest boy in his class, and he just couldn't bear having the others call him "tiny" and "shrimpy" and other things like that.

Of course he was growing all the time, but somehow he never seemed to catch up with the other boys. They were always a little taller and a little fatter.

Mother didn't have the least trouble in getting him to eat cabbage and spinach and cauliflower, for just as soon as he would say, "I don't want any," she would reply, "Well, Billy, this will help to make you big and strong; so you had better eat it." And then Billy would eat it all up and wonder just how much bigger it had really made him.

It was the same with rice pudding and other things that Billy didn't like; but even though he ate them all in the hope of growing bigger more quickly, it never seemed to make a great deal of difference.

Every now and then mother would stand Billy up against the wall, and, placing a ruler flat on his head, she would make a little mark on the wallpaper. Billy used to watch that mark with great interest, and whenever he saw it had gone up a teeny-weeny bit, he was very happy.

83

"Don't worry so much about it, Billy," mother would say. "You haven't started to grow yet. Wait until you are a little older; then you'll begin to shoot up like a bean-stalk."

Billy tried hard to believe what mother said, but the happy days of rapid growth seemed a long time coming.

Then one day something very funny happened.

I am not quite sure of the time, but I think it was on a Sabbath afternoon, not long after mother and Billy had come back from church. The house had been quiet for a while, and then mother, who had been resting, was roused by the sound of running water. She listened for a while, and then, as the water continued to run, she went downstairs and quietly opened the kitchen door.

What do you suppose she saw?

Well, there was Billy standing in front of the sink, rubbing and scrubbing away at his hands while a big soapy lather covered his arms.

"Billy dear!" cried mother. "What in the world are you doing?"

Billy hardly looked around. Instead he went right on with his vigorous hand-washing.

"Billy!" called mother again, "what are you doing?"

"I am getting big and strong," said Billy very solemnly.

Mother nearly laughed, but she didn't. She just said, "But how, Billy? I don't quite understand."

"Teacher told us all about it in Sabbath school this morning," said Billy. "And it says so in the Bible."

A broad smile crept over mother's face.

"But, Billy," she began, "what did the teacher say? I never heard about it before. Tell me—"

"It's all right," said Billy, still very earnest. "Teacher

said that the Bible said that if we had clean hands, we
would grow big and strong. I learned the verse off by
heart, I did."

"You did!" said mother. "Oh, do tell me, dear. I
would so like to know it."

"It is Job 17:9," recited Billy, "and it says, 'The
righteous also shall hold on his way, and he that hath clean
hands shall be stronger and stronger.' So there."

For a moment mother didn't know what to say. And
there were tears in her eyes as she threw her arms around
Billy's neck and kissed him.

"Don't you believe it?" asked Billy, rinsing off the
soap and showing hands that had not been so clean for a
very long time.

"Of course, of course," said mother. "I am sure God
will keep His promise to you when you have such faith.
But shall I tell you something else that that verse means?"

"Yes," said Billy.

"Well," said mother, "it means that we should not only
keep our hands clean of ordinary dirt, and inkstains, and
things like that, but we should also keep them from being
stained by wrong deeds and unkind actions. He wants us
always to use our hands to help, to build, to lift, and to do
all the kind deeds we can. Then indeed shall we grow
'stronger and stronger' in character, which really matters
most, after all."

Billy was still drying his hands.

"But don't you think, mother," he said, "that if I do
all that, and really keep my hands clean, it will help me
to get big and strong, too?"

"Yes, dear, I am sure it will," said mother.

And she was right.

A Tornado on Its Way, Marked by the Funnel-Shaped Cloud

86

Saved From the Storm

✦~~~~~~~~~~~~~~~~~~~~~~~~~~~~~~~✦

THE evening had been so warm and sultry that everyone was hot and tired. So was little Jessie; and when
mother told her to go to bed, she was actually glad to go.

But when the light was put out, she was just a little bit
frightened, for from far away in the distance came the
long rolling of thunder, and now and then the whole room
was lighted up with bright flashes of lightning.

Jessie didn't like storms; so she shut her eyes tight and
said a little prayer, asking Jesus to take care of her.

Then the rain came. Down and down it came, and
while it was raining little Jessie went to sleep.

How long she slept she didn't know. It seemed like a
minute, though it must have been hours. Then something
woke her, something startling and terrifying. It was mother's
voice, and she was frightened.

"Jessie, Jessie, quick, wake up!" mother was saying.

As Jessie awoke she heard another sound, the most
dreadful noise she had heard in all her life. It was a terrible
roaring like one great peal of thunder that would not stop.

Jessie was very much frightened now.

"Oh, mamma, mamma, what's the matter? What is
it?" she cried.

"It's a tornado, and it's right upon us," said mother.
"We must pray, darling. I'll wake daddy and get him to
pray, too,"

Daddy awoke with a start, and jumped out of bed. He guessed at once what was wrong.

They knelt down by the bed, mother on one side of Jessie, daddy on the other, their arms crossed over the little girl's head as though to protect her from danger.

By this time the fearful roaring seemed right overhead, and there were other sounds now as of windows being shattered and things being torn to pieces.

"Dear Jesus, please take care of us," one of them began.

Crash! There was a terrific noise as the house next door was smashed by the fury of the wind.

"Dear Jesus, please don't let the storm—"

Crash! Another awful sound told that the house on the other side had gone now.

Crash! Now it was the house across the street.

"O Jesus, help! Save us, please save us!"

So they prayed, while all the time those loving, sheltering arms were close over Jessie's head.

And above those arms were other arms, stronger still and yet more loving—the everlasting arms of God.

When the storm had passed, the light of morning revealed a scene of awful desolation, with trees uprooted and the wreckage of houses strewn all around. For a block and a half every building had been smashed, with one exception—the house where Jessie, mother, and daddy had prayed.

Today another storm is raging in this old world. Mother and daddy are worried about it, and maybe they have already told you how serious it is. Perhaps you have read about it in the newspapers or listened to someone talking about it over the radio.

In some ways it is worse than a tornado, for as it roars

International

After the Storm

over nation after nation, it is leaving behind a terrible trail of ruin and sorrow. It is making many people homeless, and poor, and very, very sad.

In many countries millions have lost almost everything they possessed as the hurricane of war has struck them.

It is enough to frighten anyone, but if we love Jesus, we need not be afraid, for we can hear His lovely voice speaking words of comfort and cheer. Even now He seems to be saying to us: "Fear thou not; for I am with thee:

be not dismayed; for I am thy God: I will strengthen thee; yea, I will help thee; yea, I will uphold thee with the right hand of My righteousness."   Isa. 41:10.

Fear not!   How He says it over and over again!

"Fear not: for I have redeemed thee."   Isa. 43:1.

Carlo Vogel, Artist

Jesus Loves Little Children, and They Love Him

"Fear not, little flock; for it is your Father's good pleasure to give you the kingdom." Luke 12:32.

He doesn't want us to be afraid. Rather, He wants us to trust Him always, with all our hearts. No matter what happens, He would have us keep calm and confident, believing that in His own good time He will cause the right to triumph and peace to prevail.

Then He whispers to us these precious promises:

"He that dwelleth in the secret place of the Most High shall abide under the shadow of the Almighty. . . . Thou shalt not be afraid for the terror by night; nor for the arrow that flieth by day. . . . Because thou hast made the Lord, which is my refuge, even the Most High, thy habitation; there shall no evil befall thee, neither shall any plague come nigh thy dwelling." Ps. 91:1-10.

"Underneath are the everlasting arms," He assures us. Arms of love, sheltering love, under us and over us always, just like the arms that sheltered little Jessie.

As the storm comes nearer, Jesus will not forget His promises. And let us not forget to pray, and keep on praying till the skies are clear again.

Then one day the storm will pass. Peace will come again, glorious, eternal peace; and we shall see, so clearly then, how Jesus has done all things well.

Jesus Telling His Disciples About His Return

H. Hofmann, Artist

Jesus Telling His Disciples About His Return

Talking Drums

MORE than a thousand years before anyone had heard about radio, native peoples in Africa were able to speak to each other over long distances by means of talking drums.

I don't mean that they had drums that could speak as you and I speak; yet they talked just the same!

You see, in every village men were trained to play the drums so skillfully that messages could be sent by the sound that the drums made.

Some of the drums were so large that their sound would travel as far as twenty miles or more. And as soon as the drums would begin to sound in one village, the drummer in the next village would take up the message and begin to sound it out on his drum. So from village to village the word would go until the whole countryside had heard it.

When really big things happened, the news would be sent in this way all across the whole great continent.

It is said that when Queen Victoria died, and the news was cabled from England to West Africa, natives living hundreds of miles from railways and telegraph lines immediately began talking of the death of the "Great White Queen." They heard the news even before government officials, by means of the talking drums.

When the city of Khartoum fell and General Gordon died at his post, natives in Sierra Leone, thousands of miles away, were talking of it the same day!

The largest drums are made from huge, hollowed-out tree trunks. Sometimes these measure as much as twelve feet long and five feet wide. Think of a drum that size! No wonder the sound of it carries twenty miles!

Wouldn't you like to hear drums like this being played?

Someone who has heard them all his life has said: "Shuddering down the wind come their voices. . . . Boom-tap-boom! Dumm . . . dum . . . t-rat . . . t-t-r-r-rat! Bo-o-o-o-om!"

You can almost hear them, can't you? I wonder what they are saying. Perhaps some awful disaster has happened, a flood or a fire, or some great chief has died.

The drums of Africa are still talking today. Perhaps you will hear them someday.

But there are other talking drums sounding all around the world today—drums that you can hear if you will listen. And I don't mean the drums of war, although you can hear those too plainly now.

I am thinking of other drums. We might call them God's drums. And they are talking very loudly, bringing news, not only of things that have happened, but of things that are going to happen.

Boom! Boom! Boom!

"Shuddering down the wind come their voices."

Yes, all the terrible things that are happening in the world today, all the suffering of so many people, all the sorrows of so many fathers and mothers and little children, all the smashing of so many little homes, are shouting a message to us.

Boom! Boom! Boom!

The deep, resonant sound circles the whole great globe. "Wake up!" it says to us. "Wake up! Be on the watch for something that is coming soon!" "Watch and pray: for ye know not when the time is!"

Jesus knew all about these things, and He told us that there would be "talking drums" in these days; only He called them by a different name. "There shall be *signs*," He said, "in the sun, and in the moon, and in the stars; and upon the earth distress of nations, with perplexity; the sea and the waves roaring; men's hearts failing them for fear, and for looking after those things which are coming on the earth: for the powers of heaven shall be shaken." Luke 21:25, 26.

In the last days, said Jesus, everything would talk to us —the sun, the moon, the stars, the sea, the people, the heavens, and the earth. Talking drums thundering out their warning of His coming!

And He added, "When these things begin to come to pass, then look up, and lift up your heads; for your redemption draweth nigh." Verse 28.

What a wonderful thing it is that God is trying to tell us now! Are you listening? Can you hear the drums?

And if we can hear them, and their warning message, what shall we do about it?

Shall we not look up into His face and say to Him, "Jesus, I'm glad that you are coming again. I am so anxious to see you. I want to live in the beautiful land of peace you are preparing for those who love you. I love you, too. And I want to be ready to meet you when you come. Please make me ready. Take all sin out of my heart. Help me to be good today and every day until you come again."

Won't you say that? And say it now?

If you do, there will be no doubt concerning what will

happen in that great day, for we are told that "He shall send His angels with a great sound of a trumpet, and they shall gather together His elect from the four winds, from one end of heaven to the other." Matt. 24:31.

That means that they will be looking for you! The angels looking for you! How very wonderful! And they will find you. I know they will. And they will take us all home to that beautiful land where there will be no more war and "no more death, neither sorrow, nor crying, neither shall there be any more pain." Rev. 21:4.

Come, happy day!

International   Arthur Twiddle, Artist

Jesus Will Be Looking for You

UNCLE ARTHUR'S
BEDTIME STORIES
Eighteenth Series

With Every Good Wish

To --

From --

*Uncle Arthur Telling a Bedtime Story to Little Friends Who Have Been Looking
at the Seventeen Other Volumes in This Series*

Uncle Arthur's

BEDTIME STORIES

(*EIGHTEENTH SERIES*)

BY ARTHUR S. MAXWELL

"Who is the greatest in the
kingdom of heaven? And Jesus
called a little child unto Him."
Matt. 18:1, 2.

REVIEW AND HERALD PUBLISHING ASSOCIATION

TAKOMA PARK, WASHINGTON, D. C.

PRINTED IN U. S. A.

CONTENTS

PREFACE

WHEN you see "Eighteenth Series" on the cover of "Bedtime Stories," you know that eighteen years have gone by since the first little edition of Number One came from the press in 1924.

How many copies have been sold since then? Who can tell? We have definite figures totaling six and a half million, but in addition there are all those sold in countries still at war, from which no news can come.

And, by the way, it is a very lovely thought that "Bedtime Stories" are being read by thousands of children of many nations and languages whose fathers, alas, are called to fight one another on the battlefields of the world. Perhaps, who knows, they may play some little part in bringing peace at last.

Every now and then somebody tells us of some new language in which "Bedtime Stories" have appeared. The total number of languages in which they have already been printed is more than twenty.

In this volume the original plan has been carefully followed. Every story has a character-building purpose. Every story is original; indeed, we have traveled twenty thousand miles to find them! What is more, every story has come out of the heart of some little child. The remarkable answers to children's prayers, of which there are several in this volume, are guaranteed to be genuine experiences told to us personally by the children themselves or by their parents.

That this book, like those that have preceded it, may bring much joy and blessing to all who read, both young and old, and that it may be filled with the message of the love of God for the children of men, is the sincere desire of—

THE AUTHOR.

Betty Reading Her Bible

6

The Book That Would Not Burn

HOW Betty loved her daddy! And somehow, even though she had seven brothers and sisters, she felt that her daddy loved her best of all. Perhaps that was because she was the eldest in the family and so, of course, daddy had had longer to love her than all the rest.

Daddy, by the way, was a minister, and among his most precious possessions was a Bible that a very dear friend had given him many years ago. He always used this Bible when he was studying, or preaching, and, of course, in family worship.

One day when Betty and her daddy were alone in his study, he suddenly became very solemn.

"Betty," he said quietly, "none of us knows what is going to happen in the future, but if anything should go wrong—er—if anything should happen to me—"

"Don't say that, daddy," said Betty, with a worried look on her face. "Nothing must ever happen to you."

"Of course, we hope not," replied daddy with a smile, "but just in case something sometime should happen to me, I want you to have my Bible. It is to be yours, always."

"Oh, thank you, daddy," cried Betty. "I shall prize it above everything else all my life."

From that day on, even though daddy continued to use his Bible as he always had, Betty watched over it

7

with special care.   Every now and then she would go into the study and dust the Book tenderly, then open it to read some message for herself.   She felt that it was her book already, and that it would be a precious memory of her father forever.

Not long after this daddy fell ill.   Month after month went by, and he became steadily worse.   Then one day he said good-by to everybody and passed away.

Betty was heartbroken, and her only consolation was the thought that daddy had given her his Bible, his most precious possession, for herself.   She left it there on his study table, where it lay surrounded by all the other books in the library, like a king amid his courtiers.   Every day she would tiptoe into the room and touch it reverently, silently turning its sacred pages.   Tears would come to her eyes as she remembered that this was *his* book, and that he had given it to her.

Then one day something dreadful happened.

Betty was visiting in the home of a girl friend across the road.   While they were talking together, they heard the fire alarm, and one said to the other, "There must be a fire somewhere; I wonder whose house it is this time?"

They went to the window to look out, and suddenly Betty screamed.

"It's our house!" she cried.   "Oh, look at the flames!"

They ran outside and tried to cross the road, but already a large crowd had gathered, and two fire engines were busy pumping water on the flames, while helmeted firemen were smashing windows and trying to carry out what furniture they could.

Betty struggled to break through the crowd, but the neighbors held her back.   She appealed to a policeman.

"There's something in there I've got to save!" she cried, beside herself with anxiety.

"Ah, missy," he said, "you can't go in there. It's just a roaring furnace. You'd be burned to a cinder."

"But I've got to go!" cried Betty. "I've got to go! Let me go!"

"No, dear, I couldn't let you go in there," said the kindly policeman. "I'm sorry, but it's impossible. See, even the firemen are leaving now."

Betty turned away heartbroken. It was of no use. Of course it was of no use. She could see that. But, oh, her Bible! If only she had stayed at home!

Away in the crowd, yet feeling more alone than she had ever felt in all her life, she thought of Jesus.

"O Lord," she cried, wringing her hands, "save my Bible, daddy's Bible. Don't let it burn. Please don't let it get burned!"

And so she prayed, while the angry flames roared through the building, turning the home she loved so dearly into a heap of ugly ashes. Two hours after the fire had started there was nothing left but two gaunt chimneys and some blackened, smoldering timbers. Roof, bedrooms, dining room, kitchen, study, all had vanished.

It was some time after this before even members of the family were allowed to wander through the ruins, but Betty was among the first. She hurried to where the study had been. She knew the place well, and it was still clearly marked by remnants of half-burned books which had belonged to her father's library.

What a terrible sight! What would daddy have said!

She came to some charred pieces of wood which she recognized had once been a desk, *his* desk. With more tenderness than ever, she moved them and peered beneath.

She gasped. What was that? Could it be? Could it possibly be?

Yes, it was. Her Bible. Daddy's Bible!

With a cry of joy she picked it up and turned its pages with an eagerness she had never felt before.

There was not a mark of fire upon it, not the shadow of a burn upon the cover or the inside!

I know it is true. Betty herself told me about it. And she told me something else. She said that that Book of hers, so marvelously preserved in the fire, became the center of the new home that the family finally built. All the children turned to it as never before. They listened to its message as they never had in all their lives. All of them gave their hearts to God. And even today, though they have all grown up and scattered over the world, they still come back home as often as they can to gaze once more upon the Bible that was saved from the fire, the wonderful Book that would not burn.

How the Cows Came Home

THE meeting was over. I had told stories to the children and preached to the big people and shaken hands with everybody at the door until I was just about tired out. Then, when I thought the church was empty, I walked to the very front seat and sat down to rest.

Then the most delightful thing happened.

Just as I was about to shut my eyes and take a short nap, the silence was broken by the patter of little feet. I thought for a moment that someone had come back for a Bible or a hymnbook that had been left behind, and that I wouldn't need to wake up. But no, the pattering came nearer and nearer, and pretty soon, round the corner of my pew, came a dear little girl all dressed up in her Sabbath-go-to-meeting best. At the moment I guessed she might be six or seven years old, and I wasn't very far wrong.

As she turned the corner she slowed up a little and then, very demurely, she walked over to where I was sitting.

"Uncle," she said, whispering in my ear, "I want to tell you a story."

"Why, that's lovely," I said to her. "But tell me your name first of all."

"My name's Margie," she said.

"That's a beautiful name," I replied. "And how old are you?"

"I'm seven," she said, "and I want to tell you about my grandma and—and her cows."

11

"What happened to them?"

"Well," she said, "you know, uncle, I have to go and look after my grandma sometimes. She lives on a little farm of her own just out of town, and sometimes, when she is not feeling very well, I go and help her."

"How very good of you," I said. "And do you look after the cows, too?"

"Oh, yes, of course," said Margie very solemnly. "I look after grandma and the cows."

"And what happened?" I asked again.

"Well, uncle, one day when I was over at the farm, looking after grandma and the cows, what do you suppose I saw?"

"I couldn't imagine," I said.

"Well, as I looked out of the kitchen window," she said, a little more loudly, "I saw one of grandma's cows walking out of the pasture onto the highway. Somebody had left the gate open."

"How very terrible!" I said. "And then what happened?"

"Well, uncle, a second cow followed the first cow and then another and another until all of them were out on the highway, running downtown as fast as they could go."

"Dear, oh, dear!" I exclaimed. "But maybe they wanted to go shopping."

"Of course not," she said, smiling.

"But what did you do?" I asked, more solemnly.

"I ran out of the house as fast as I could go, but by the time I got to the highway the cows were far away. I shouted to them to come back, but they wouldn't listen to me. They just kept on running."

"And what did you do next?"

"There wasn't anything I could do," said Margie. "However fast I might have run, I could never have got in front of them and turned them around."

"And so?"

"Well, uncle, do you know what I did?"

"I couldn't imagine."

Margie's voice became still more of a whisper.

"Uncle, I got down on my knees on the highway and I shut my eyes tight and prayed, 'Please, Jesus, make the naughty cows come home!' "

"You dear little girl," I said, "how very, very beautiful! And then what happened?"

"Well, uncle, do you know, when I opened my eyes again, those naughty cows had turned around and were trotting back up the highway. They came to where I was standing, and they turned in at the gate, just as though they knew they should never have gone out. And when the last one had gone back into the field, I rushed over to the gate and shut it quickly."

"Good girl!" I cried, "and then?"

"Then I ran indoors and told my grandma all about it, and how Jesus had answered my prayer."

Bless her little heart! As long as I live I shall remember the picture she painted for me that morning—of a little girl kneeling on the hard, concrete highway, with hands folded and eyes tight shut, praying, "Jesus, make the naughty cows come home!"

Faith like that sets all the angels in heaven to work for us. And God would see the sun grow cold rather than leave such a prayer unanswered.

This Little Boy Seems to Like Jam, Too!

14

Jimmy and the Jam Jars

JIMMY had a great liking for jam. Indeed, he loved it. In this, of course, he was not very different from most other little boys of his age—and girls, too, for that matter. But Jimmy, well, he couldn't even look at a jam pot without feeling all stirred up inside.

Now it so happened that one fine day mother had spent the whole morning making strawberry jam. She had filled twenty or thirty jars, some large, some small, and by early afternoon they were all standing in neat rows in the top of her kitchen cabinet.

What a pleasing picture they made, with big strawberries clearly to be seen amid the thick red jelly that held them all together!

Happy to think that her task was done, with all the dirty dishes and saucepans cleaned and put away, mother decided to go out visiting for a little while.

"Jimmy," she said, as she came downstairs with her hat and coat on, "I'm going across to see Mrs. Brown for a few minutes. I'll be back soon. Be a good boy while I'm away."

"All right, mother," said Jimmy. "Don't worry. I'll be good."

"You have plenty of things to play with, haven't you?"

"Oh, yes, mother," said Jimmy. "I think I'll play with my trains."

"That's a good idea," said mother. "And, by the way,

15

Jimmy, I think it would be better for you not to go in the kitchen."

"All right, mother.   Why?"

"Oh, well," said mother, thinking of her newly made jam, "just because—er—well, I think you had better not. Now good-by, Jimmy, and be good."

"Good-by, mother," said Jimmy, waving his hand and then running to play with his trains.

Unfortunately, mother was gone much longer than she expected.   It often happens that way, you know.

Meanwhile Jimmy got tired of playing with his trains and turned to his bricks, then to his trucks.   At last he decided he didn't want to play with anything any more, and started to walk around the house, looking for something to do.

From the kitchen there still came the sweet odor of newly made jam, and Jimmy thought it was a very nice smell indeed.   He went to the kitchen door and peeked in. Everything was very clean and tidy, and he could not see any particular reason why his mother should not want him to go in there.   So in he went and wandered around.

As he walked about he kept saying to himself, "I wonder where mamma put all that jam."

Suddenly he looked upward, and, lo, there it was, all of it, on the three top shelves of the kitchen cabinet.   The bright-red jars looked like rows of old-time soldiers such as one sees sometimes in picture books.

"What a fine lot of jam!" exclaimed Jimmy.

He looked and looked and looked.

"I wonder," he said to himself after a while, "if mother would mind if I were to open the cupboard door and look at it a little closer?"

As mother wasn't there to answer his question, he decided to answer it himself, and proceeded to carry a stool over to the base of the cabinet.

Now it is just as well to remember that many kitchen cabinets are made in two parts. There is a top half and a bottom half, and the one sits lightly on the other. Unfortunately, Jimmy didn't know that.

Standing on the stool, he was just able to reach the knob on the glass door, which he gently pulled. The two doors swung open, and Jimmy stood there, admiring the wonderful array of jam jars.

"I wonder," he said to himself, "if mother would mind if I were to taste just a little bit—just a very little bit. There is so much that I don't think mother would even notice it, and I'm sure she wouldn't mind."

So Jimmy reached up and began trying to open one of the jam jars.

Alas! Just at that moment the stool slipped away from under his feet. To save himself Jimmy clutched desperately at one of the shelves of the cabinet and—

Crash!

In an instant Jimmy, cabinet, and jam jars had become one dreadful, sticky mess upon the kitchen floor.

At that very moment mother was nearing the house, on her way home from Mrs. Brown's. Hearing the crash, she dashed indoors, only to find Jimmy lying on the floor buried beneath the remains of her strawberry jam.

"Oh, my poor Jimmy!" she said, rushing toward him. "He's dead. I'm sure he's dead. My poor dear little Jimmy!"

But Jimmy wasn't dead. At least, something was moving under the cabinet, and, as mother lifted it up, Jimmy stood to his feet. What a sight he was! He looked for all the world like a piece of bread and butter spread with jam. He was covered with jam from head to foot. There was jam in his hair, and jam on his shirt, jam on his trousers, and jam on his shoes.

Mother took Jimmy over to the sink and began to wash the jam out of his eyes and ears. Then she found that he wasn't really hurt at all. Not a single cut anywhere, despite all that broken glass!

Then a new note came into mother's voice. It was an ominous note.

"You naughty little boy!" she cried. "How dare you disobey me like that! Look at all my jam! Look at my cabinet all broken to pieces! You bad boy, you!"

At this point mother began walking toward the stairs, with Jimmy's hand held tightly in hers.

Just what happened upstairs I will leave you to imagine, but Jimmy told me—yes, believe it or not, he told me himself—that in all the years that have gone by since then he has never forgotten what happened that afternoon, and—what matters most of all—he has never, never disobeyed his mother from that day to this.

The Boy With Twelve Friends

THE BOY WITH TWELVE FRIENDS

IT was a fine summer morning as thirteen boys from a certain church school started off together for a day's outing in the mountains.

What a wonderful day it was going to be! They had looked forward to it for a long time and planned a thousand things to do. And now at last the day had come, and here they were, with their lunches in baskets and paper bags, and bright smiles on their faces, all ready for the journey. How they shouted, and how they teased one another!

They crowded into three cars driven by older friends, and away they went, happy as could be. Higher and higher they climbed up the mountain road, until at last they came to the beautiful forest where they all loved to go for their special treats. Here they jumped out, and the drivers, waving good-by, returned to the city.

Now they were alone, thirteen boys all ready for the greatest day of their little lives. They wandered among the trees down to the river and followed it to the lake. There someone suggested that they might as well eat in such a pretty spot, and it didn't take more than one suggestion like that to set all of them to opening their lunches.

There was silence for a while. Everybody was too busy eating to talk. But at last David, who was a leader among them, spoke up and asked what the others would like to do after lunch.

"Let's swing on the wild vines," they all called out together, and it was clear as day that this was what they
wanted to do most of all.

"All right," cried David. "Has everybody finished eating? If so, then let's be off to the vines."

You see, the boys had all been in this forest several times
before, and they remembered that in a certain part of it there
were some strange wild vines that not only grew around the
trees, but actually spread from tree to tree until all were
bound together as in some tropical jungle. Between the
branches of some trees the vines would hang in great loops
like the ropes of a swing, and the boys were not slow to
recognize the possibilities.

There were so many of these loops that there were
swings for all of them and more to spare. Soon all thirteen
boys were hanging on to the vines, swinging to their hearts'
content.

It was such fun, with each boy trying to swing higher
than the rest. If one of them did not like the swing he had
chosen, he just moved on and found a better one.

Sometimes a boy would climb quite a good way up a
tree in order to reach one of the larger and longer loops,
and then he would slide down till he reached the middle
and swing till he was tired.

Presently David called out, "Look at that beauty over
there," pointing to an unusually fine vine that drooped
temptingly from one branch to another. It was fairly high
up, but several made a rush to get to it first. David, however, was ahead, and, making a great leap, seized the vine
and was soon swinging away, while the others looked on.

Suddenly, to their horror, they heard a terrible rending
sound as the vine broke loose from one of the trees. At that

moment David was in the middle of a mighty swing, and, crashing down to the ground, hit his head upon a rock.

"Oh!" exclaimed all the boys at once as they ran toward the place where David lay on the ground. They tried to lift him up, but he did not move; and suddenly the dreadful thought came to them that he might be dead.

By this time all twelve boys had gathered round, looking down at the limp form, and shuddering as they saw the blood trickling from the wound on his head.

"What shall we do?" exclaimed one. "Someone had better run and get help," cried another. But nobody moved.

Then somebody else spoke. "Let us kneel down and pray for him," he said. "It is all we can do."

"Yes," said the others, very solemnly. "Let's pray."

And there in that lonely forest these twelve boys knelt upon the ground around David and asked God for help. First one prayed and then another, and another, until at last all twelve had sent up a brief, halting petition to the great Friend of children above.

Now it may sound unbelievable, I know, but when that last simple little prayer had been said, David began to move.

"Look!" they cried. "He's not dead after all."

Then one of them ran for some water, and they bathed David's face. Soon he opened his eyes, and then they gave him a drink. By and by he sat up, then stood up, and after a while they partly carried him, partly led him, back to the highway, to where they waited for a car to take him home.

Years have passed since then, but not one of those boys will ever forget that strange and beautiful prayer meeting in the forest. And every one of them agrees with David that it is a fine thing to have twelve friends to pray for you when you need help.

Teaching Dolly Her Lessons

Gladys and the Glue Bottle

GLADYS and Jane—the little girl who lived next door —were playing happily with their dolls. Suddenly something terrible happened.

Just how it happened nobody knows, but before anybody could do anything about it, the beautiful baby doll that Gladys prized so much had slipped out of Jane's arms and crashed upon the floor.

"Oh, Jane!" cried Gladys. "You've dropped my baby doll! And it's broken. Jane, how could you!"

"I am so sorry," said Jane. "I didn't mean to."

Gladys picked up the doll and looked it over carefully.

"Look, Jane," she said sorrowfully, "its head is broken. I could cry!"

"Oh!" sighed Jane, as if it had been a real baby that had been hurt. "But don't cry, Gladys, please don't, or I shall cry, too. What shall we do about it?"

Now some little girls would have started to quarrel over a calamity like this, but not Gladys and Jane. They loved each other too much for that, and now all that Gladys said was, "Let's see if we can mend it."

"Mend it? Do you think we could?" asked Jane.

"I think so," said Gladys, trying to put the pieces together. "If only we had some glue!"

"I know where there is some," said Jane. "I saw a bottle downstairs. I'll go and get it."

23

Off she ran, anxious to do all she could to make amends for dropping the precious doll.

Very soon she was back again, with a rather dirty old bottle of glue in her hand.

"It looks very old," said Gladys. "I hope the glue will stick properly."

"I hope so," said Jane, trying hard to open the bottle; "but the cork won't come out."

"Let me try," said Gladys.

But Gladys couldn't move it either. Then Jane had another try, and presently Gladys wrestled with it again.

"What shall we do?" she said. "We could have had the dolly all fixed by now. I'm going downstairs to ask daddy to open it."

So downstairs she went with the glue bottle in her hand.

Daddy tried his very best to open it, but he, too, failed.

"Take it to uncle," he said. "His hands are stronger than mine."

So Gladys took the bottle to uncle and asked him to open it. But he couldn't, either.

"It's no use, Gladys; that bottle might just as well be thrown away," he said. "We'll get another one for you when the stores are open."

Gladys took the bottle from uncle and walked upstairs to her bedroom. "Sorry, Jane, but nobody can open it. Uncle says he'll buy us a new bottle of glue when the stores open."

"But we want to mend the dolly now," said Jane.

"Yes," said Gladys, "we must." And then, dropping her voice to a whisper, she added, "Do you know, Jane, I know somebody who could open this glue bottle."

"Do you?" asked Jane. "Who is it?"

Gladys whispered in her ear, and Jane whispered back, "Yes, Gladys, why didn't we think of that before?"

Now if you could have peeped into that bedroom a few minutes later you would have seen a most beautiful sight, for there on their knees beside two little chairs were those two dear girls, asking Jesus to open that glue bottle!

"Dear Jesus," said Gladys, "dolly's head is broken and needs fixing. We must have some glue. We can't open the bottle, neither can daddy, nor uncle, nor anybody, but I know you can. Won't you please open it for us? Amen."

When they rose from their knees, Jane started to walk over to the glue bottle to try the cork, but Gladys stopped her. "No," she said, in a loud whisper, "we must give Him a chance to get it open!"

So there they both stood for two or three minutes in absolute silence, without speaking a word, waiting for Jesus to work for them!

Now it may seem a very strange thing to some, and quite unbelievable, but when Gladys picked up that bottle from the table, and twisted the cork with her tiny fingers, it came right out!

Then, without a doubt in their hearts that their prayer had been answered, they went calmly on mending the broken dolly.

By and by they went downstairs and showed the dolly to mother and father and uncle.

"But where did you get the glue?" they asked.

"Out of the bottle," they said.

Then they told the wonderful story of what had happened upstairs. Nobody said a word for a while; they were too amazed to speak.

26

What a Hit!

Seventeen Cowards

BILL came rushing into the house and flopped down in a chair, breathless. He looked scared out of his life.

At that moment father came into the room, too. "Whatever's the matter, Bill?" he inquired anxiously.

"Oh, nothing," said Bill.

"Yes, there is," said father. "I can tell by the look on your face. What has happened?"

"Oh, well, dad," said Bill, wriggling uncomfortably on his chair, "you see, we were all playing ball up there on that vacant lot near old Mrs. Boliger's. You know where it is, dad, about half a mile down the street from here."

"Yes, I know it well," said father. "I used to play on it myself when I was a boy."

"Well, dad, the ball—" hesitated Bill.

"I know what you are going to say," said father. "The ball went through Mrs. Boliger's window."

"Well, yes, dad. That's what happened. How did you know?"

"I just guessed," said father. "But, say, Bill, why are you so scared?"

"I'm not really scared, dad," said Bill, "but, you know, Mrs. Boliger is such a mean old woman. She makes such a fuss about things like that."

"Well, what did you all do after the window was broken?"

"We ran away."

"You ran away!"

"Yes."

"Well, how many boys were playing?"

"Seventeen."

"And you mean to tell me that all seventeen of you ran away, afraid of what some elderly woman might say to you?"

"Yes, dad," said Bill, hanging his head a little.

"Well," said father, "all I can say is that I think you were just seventeen cowards, that's all."

Bill didn't like that, but he knew in his heart that the charge was true. For a moment he tried to defend himself.

"But, dad, Mrs. Boliger is so awfully cranky," he said.

"It doesn't matter how cranky she is," said father. "If you boys broke her window, you should have had the courage to go and tell her you did it, and offer to pay for the damage. Why, bless your heart, it wouldn't have cost more than a few cents apiece. By the way, who hit the ball that broke the window?"

Bill hesitated. "Er-er-er—" he began.

"Now come on," said father. "There couldn't have been seventeen balls, nor could seventeen boys have smashed the window at once."

"That's right, dad."

"Then who hit the ball that broke the window?"

"I did," said Bill, very crestfallen.

"I thought so," said father, "only I wanted you to own up. And now, no matter what the others do, you must go at once to Mrs. Boliger's and tell her you are sorry."

"I couldn't, dad," cried Bill, truly alarmed. "I simply couldn't. She is such a dreadful crank."

"But you must," said father severely. "It is the only

proper thing to do. What is more, no boy of mine is going to be such a coward as not to apologize when he has done a thing like this. So get yourself cleaned up, and we'll go."

"You mean you are going to go with me?"

"Yes, I am going to go with you as far as Mrs. Boliger's front gate, and then you are going to go to the door and speak to her all by yourself."

"Oh, groans," Bill muttered to himself as he got off his chair and went to the bathroom to wash his hands and brush his hair.

By and by he came downstairs again, where father was all ready, waiting for him. Together they set out for Mrs. Boliger's.

It wasn't a very happy journey; at least, not for Bill. He couldn't have been more scared if he had been on his way to an examination, or to prison.

"Do I really have to go?" he asked after a while, breaking a painful silence.

"I'm afraid you do," said father. "There's really no other way. And you will feel a great deal happier when you have done the right thing."

Silence fell again. They walked on, Bill wishing that the distance might have been twenty miles, so father would get tired and give up.

At last they turned a corner and came to the vacant lot where the accident had taken place. Mrs. Boliger's house was in full view, and so was the broken window.

"Here we are," said father, as they reached the little white gate at the entrance to Mrs. Boliger's property. "I will wait here while you go to the house and speak to her. It is much better for you to do this little job alone. I shall be near by if you need me."

There was nothing else for Bill to do now but go on alone, but as he went up the path he felt sure that Mrs. Boliger's eyes were watching him all the way.

And all the time he kept thinking to himself, "What will she say when I confess that I was the one who broke her window?"

Bill rang the bell. It sounded loud and long, like the very knell of doom.

The door opened, and there stood Mrs. Boliger. To Bill's amazement she had a smile on her face. He had not expected that.

"How do you do?" she said in a kindly tone of voice. "What can I do for you?"

"Well—er—well—er," stuttered Bill, blushing all over, "I—er—I—er—am the boy who—er—hit the ball that—er—broke your window this afternoon."

Bill hesitated and then turned away a little as though he were waiting for a bomb to explode.

But it didn't. Instead he heard a very sweet voice saying, "I am proud of you, son. I have had my windows broken this way many, many times, but you are the very first boy who has ever come to tell me about it. You are a real little gentleman. You surely must have been brought up well. You must have a wonderful father."

And now it was father's turn to blush.

"Oh," said Bill, "that's my dad over there. He happened to come along with me."

At this, of course, father had to come forward.

"You have a fine boy here," said Mrs. Boliger. "In fact, I think he's the grandest boy I've ever met. You know, sir, no boy has ever come here before and spoken to me like this about breaking my windows."

"Well, Mrs. Boliger," said father, "Bill and I would like to pay you for putting the glass in again."

"Oh, dear, no," said Mrs. Boliger. "I wouldn't think of it. It's quite all right. I've mended so many before. And I wouldn't have this dear boy pay for one of my windows in any case."

Bill beamed with joy and pride.

They all talked together for a little while, and then father and Bill said good-by and started for home.

"I suppose," said father, "you aren't sorry you went to see her?"

"I should say not," said Bill. "Why, she was as nice as pie. I never would have dreamed that Mrs. Boliger could be like that. I wonder why the boys say that she is mean? She isn't a bit mean. She couldn't have been kinder."

"Boys say those things sometimes because they don't understand," said father. "By the way, Bill, don't you feel better now since you have done the right thing, the brave thing?"

"Do I!" said Bill. "I could jump clear over the moon!"

Out of the Mud

THIS is a very little story about a very small boy. He was only four years old when this happened; so you mustn't smile too much when you hear about it.

I will call him Tiny, for he seemed so small when he came up to speak to me one day.

It appears that Tiny's father has both a car and a trailer, and not very long ago he took Tiny away with the rest of the family for a nice long vacation.

For a time all went well and everyone was having a very happy time. Then one day father decided to turn off the main road and go exploring through a very wild district that he had never been in before. This was fun, too, while the sun continued to shine and the rough roads were still dry, but when the clouds rolled up and the rain began to tumble down, well, that was something different.

How it rained! It was worse than "cats and dogs," and soon all the land around became boggy, and the road a sea of mud. The car sank into a deep rut, and the trailer followed. It was impossible to move.

Father got out of the car to see whether he could do anything, but the mud covered his boots, while the rain soaked him to the skin.

"It's pretty bad," he said, as he got back in the car again. "I'm afraid we shall be stuck here for some time."

They were. And gradually the light began to fade as night came creeping on.

Poor Tiny began to get frightened, and in vain did

father and mother seek to comfort him. They said that there was really nothing serious to worry about, because they could sleep all night in the trailer, but Tiny would not be comforted. He didn't like the idea of staying out there on the narrow, desolate highway where something might come along in the dark and run into them. He wanted to go home, or at least to some place where he would feel safe again. So he began to pray.

It was such a simple little prayer that some people may laugh at it, but it was so earnest—just these few words: "Please, Jesus, push us out of the mud!"

By and by the rain stopped, and father got out of the car again. With his shovel he tried to dig the soft, oozy mud away from the wheels.

Meanwhile Tiny kept repeating his prayer over and over again. "Please, Jesus, push us out of the mud," "Please, Jesus, push us out of the mud," and in between praying he would watch father out of the window.

By and by, when father had almost finished clearing the wheels, a farm wagon happened to come along, and the driver towed car and trailer on to harder ground.

Tiny was overjoyed. He felt sure that this was a direct answer to his prayer, and from that day to this he has never once failed to thank Jesus for coming to the rescue. In fact, not only does he mention it in his nightly prayer, but he repeats his thanks three times a day, when he says grace at meals.

I asked him to tell me himself just exactly what he says, and here it is, without a single change:

"Amen. God bless this food. Jesus pushed us out of the mud."

Blessed, beautiful faith of a little child!

V18B5

Lionel Green

Praying for Her Daddy

34

He Felt Her Praying

+ ∿∿∿∿∿∿∿∿∿∿∿∿∿∿∿∿∿∿∿∿∿∿∿∿ +

IT happened on the night of September 21, 1938—the night of the great New England hurricane. A truck driver whom I know had been out driving all day, and was on his way home. Suddenly the storm struck in all its fury, and the great wind went roaring over the land.

So terrific was the force of this gale that tens of thousands of houses collapsed as if they had been made of cardboard. Nearly three hundred million trees were broken off or uprooted. Hundreds of thousands of telephone poles were blown down, and twenty-six thousand motorcars were smashed. Worst of all, six hundred persons lost their lives and many thousands were injured.

As my friend drove along the highway, trees and poles fell in front of him and behind him, completely hemming him in. He stepped out of the truck and was nearly knocked over by the fury of the wind.

He wondered what to do. Looking at his speedometer he calculated that he was about sixteen miles from home. Home! How much he would give to be there now! But was his home still there? Had it withstood the tempest? He thought of his wife and little girl; perhaps they needed him. Certainly they would be worrying about him. And praying for him, too, no doubt. How little Maryland loved to pray for her daddy!

He decided to abandon the truck and attempt to make his way home at any cost.

What a journey it was! Had he realized what it would be like before he started out, he would probably never have made the venture.

Every few yards there was a fallen pole to climb over or an uprooted tree to get around, and in the pitch darkness this often meant slipping into ditches filled with water or trudging across fields deep with mud. Every few moments there was a rending sound in the near-by forest as still another great tree came crashing down; and in the inky blackness it was impossible to tell where it was going to fall.

Now and then, when he felt almost exhausted, he would wonder whether he should turn back and seek again the shelter that the cab of the truck afforded. But no. Something urged him onward. In the worst moments of that awful night he thought he could see Maryland praying for him. So he struggled bravely homeward.

How many hours it took him to cover those sixteen miles I do not know, but at last he felt that he must be almost there. And look, what was that? Lights flickering! Yes, they were hurricane lamps his wife had hung out along the road to guide him back.

After that all was easy. He found the house still there, and mother and Maryland waiting up for him.

"But how did you get through?" was their question. "How could you stand the strain?"

"One thought kept me going," he said, looking down at his little daughter. "I felt she was praying for me."

And she had been—all night. Maryland told me herself.

Who knows what good a little girl may do when she prays for her daddy!

Dad Needs Me!

✦~~~~~~~~~~~~~~~~~~~~~~~~~~✦

WHILE we are still thinking about that dreadful hurricane in which Maryland's father was caught, I want to tell you about another beautiful thing that happened that same night.

Another friend of mine, a minister of the gospel, was out driving in his car at the time when, with awful suddenness, the storm broke. Instantly trees started falling all around him, one of them narrowly missing his car.

He jumped out, somewhat scared, but thankful to be alive. Then he looked around. Both ways, as far as he could see, the road was a chaos of twisted wires, broken telephone poles, and uprooted trees. He had never seen such wreckage before.

Not far away he saw another car that had been caught like his own between the falling timber, but he noticed that that driver, a fine, sturdy lad, was already busily sawing at the nearest tree.

It seemed foolish for one lone youth to be sawing away at one great tree, on such a night, when there were probably several hundred trees blocking the road between him and where he wanted to go.

But the lad sawed on with a fury of energy matched only by that of the gale itself. He seemed frantic with anxiety.

My friend clambered over some fallen trees and went up to speak to him.

37

"Why are you sawing like this, so energetically?" he asked.

The young man paused a moment and looked up.

"I've got to get through," he said. "Dad needs me."

Then he turned back to his task, sawing more strenuously, if possible, than before.

The tree was cut through and hauled out of the way. Immediately he started on another. By this time other men had turned up from near-by farms, all with saws in their hands, and had started cutting away. Little by little the road was cleared.

During a brief pause in the work my friend ventured to speak to the young man again.

"Tell me," he said, "why is it so important that you get to your father?"

"Why is it important?" replied the young man. "Because there's a big tree in front of our house, and it has probably fallen on it. Mother is away, and dad is all alone. I've just got to get through to help him."

By this time a sufficient stretch of road had been cleared in one direction for my friend to turn his car around and drive away, but, he told me, the last thing he remembers seeing as he left that spot—a picture that will remain in his mind forever—was that young man, ax in hand, hacking away furiously at the branches of yet another tree that lay between him and his father.

He had to get through to his dad!

God bless him!

Four Times as Much

JOHN had been taught by his mother to give to God one tenth of all the money he earned. It is a noble thing to do, and the Bible says that people who follow this plan with their money may always be sure of receiving a special blessing from heaven.

From the very first time that John had earned any money of his own, he had most carefully set aside one tenth for the Lord. This he had put in the collection plate at church. If he received ten cents for doing some gardening, then he saved one cent for God. If he received twenty cents for helping to wash somebody's car, then he put two cents aside in the same way.

Year by year as he grew older he continued to divide his money like this, but, by and by, as he saw many things that he wanted to buy like the other boys at school, he began to leave God out sometimes. He didn't tell mother, of course, because he knew she would be disappointed; and so that he wouldn't feel too bad about it himself, he made a note in a little book of all he knew he should pay and didn't. He told himself that someday, when he had made a great deal of money, he would pay it all up.

Of course that day did not come. It never does. And so the figures in John's little notebook grew larger and larger, and the possibility of his ever paying it became more and more remote.

Then one day he came home from school all excited with

Jesus Blessing the Loaves and Fishes Before Feeding the Multitude

the news that a very special outing had been planned. His teacher had arranged for a wonderful trip into the country, where they would have boat rides and good things to eat, and what not. The only difficulty was the expense. It was going to cost three dollars each.

"Well," said mother, "that settles it. I couldn't pay all that. If you want to go very badly, you will have to use some of your own money."

John's face fell. He did so want to go with all the others in his class, but how could he use any more of his money when he owed God so much already?

Going upstairs, he opened the drawer where he kept his pennies and the little account book, and began to count up to see how much he still had left.

Twenty-five cents, fifty cents, a dollar, one dollar fifty, one dollar seventy-five cents, two dollars.

So he counted.

Two dollars and fifty cents, two dollars seventy-five cents, three dollars.

He had enough, just enough. He could go to the outing after all!

But then he noticed the little notebook. Opening it slowly, he began counting again. And the more he counted, the more his heart sank.

Could it be possible he owed God so much?

One dollar, two dollars, three dollars!

Dreadful thought! If he paid God all he owed Him, he would have nothing left. Then he could not possibly go. What should he do?

He was getting into a terrible state of mind when the door opened softly and mother entered. Quickly he threw his money and book into the drawer and closed it.

But somehow mother guessed what was the matter. Mother always does guess right, doesn't she?

Sitting down on John's bed, mother picked up his Bible and turned the pages slowly until she came to the third chapter of the book of Malachi. And there she read those old familiar words: "Will a man rob God? Yet ye have robbed Me. But ye say, Wherein have we robbed Thee? In tithes and offerings. . . . Bring ye all the tithes into the storehouse, that there may be meat in Mine house, and prove Me now herewith, saith the Lord of hosts, if I will not open you the windows of heaven, and pour you out a blessing, that there shall not be room enough to receive it."

John had heard mother read these verses many times before, but somehow this time they made a deeper impression on his mind than ever before.

"Mother," he said, "I've decided not to go to that outing."

"You have, dear?" said mother. "Why?"

"Well, I might as well tell you. I have just three dollars saved up, and I owe it all to God. I haven't paid my tithe since I don't know when, and I'm going to pay it now instead of going to the outing. I wish you would take this money, so that I won't be tempted to spend it."

John passed over his precious three dollars to mother, who, for a moment, hardly knew what to say.

"I think," she said after a pause, "I think you have made the right decision, John, and I am sure that somehow it will all come out right. God does such wonderful things, you know, when we try to please Him. And when He opens the windows of heaven, He usually opens them wide."

The next few days were hard days for John. It seemed as though every few minutes some boy or girl would ask him if he were going to the outing, and he would have to reply, "No, not this time, thank you." And then he would be asked, "Why not?" and he would have to try to explain without really telling them anything.

At last the outing day arrived. This, thought John, would be the hardest day of all—to see everybody going away and have to stay behind himself.

And then, early that very morning, the postman called. He had a letter for John. It was from a relative living in the West Indies. Inside was a check for twelve dollars— exactly four times as much as the tithe John had given to God. John went to the outing after all. Indeed, he was the happiest boy there. The windows of heaven had opened again.

Ewing Galloway   *Study Hard Each Day, and You Will Not Have to Fear When Examination Day Comes*

Tom's Mistake

I T'S terrible!" exclaimed mother, looking over the report that Tom had just brought in from school. "Why, look at the marks that you have for spelling. Surely you must be the worst in the class."

"I suppose I am," said Tom sadly. "I just can't spell, Mum; it's no good trying."

"Don't talk like that," said mother. "Of course you could spell if you really tried hard. The trouble with you is that you are too careless. You don't think enough. I shall have to speak to your teacher about it and see what can be done. Anyhow, I hope you will never bring home another report as bad as this."

"Oh, well," said Tom, "I suppose spelling doesn't matter very much anyway."

"But it does matter," said mother firmly. "If you talk like that, Tom, you will never get anywhere in life. You must make up your mind that you are going to spell properly. That is the first thing to do."

Tom listened, but mother's good counsel did not make very much impression upon his mind. In fact, he didn't think at all about spelling until the next examination.

Then it was that his mother's words came back very forcibly to his mind. He recalled that she had said he was not to bring home another bad report like the last one. But how could he make this one any different? He had made no preparation; in fact, he hadn't even looked over the words that the teacher had given the class to study.

Now the teacher had the list of words in her hands. She was about to read them out to the class. The students already had their pencils in their hands.

What shall I do? thought Tom. I am sure I shall not know how to spell one of them!

"The first word," said the teacher, "is expedition."

"Expedition," said Tom to himself, biting his pencil. "Expedition, expedition. However does it go?"

Just then he saw the boy in front of him writing fast, and the temptation came to Tom to look over his shoulder.

Anything was better, he thought, than going home to mother with a bad report card. So he looked.

The boy in front had written "ex-pe-dishon." So Tom copied it exactly, "ex-pe-dishon."

"The next word," said the teacher, "is telephone."

Tom copied it, "telefone."

And so on to the end of the list. Tom and the boy in front of him were the only ones with all the words wrong.

In due time Tom arrived home with his report card, which was worse than his report had ever been before.

"What does this mean?" asked mother.

"It means," said Tom very soberly, "that I made a big mistake."

"What mistake?" asked mother.

Tom hung his head. "I copied off the wrong guy."

"Copied!" cried mother, "copied! What do you mean by copied? Why, I would rather you came home with no marks at all than that you should do such a thing as that."

"Don't worry, mother," said Tom. "I've learned my lesson all right. I never did it before, and you can be sure I shall never copy again."

The Stoneboat

THIS is a story about a strange sort of boat that never floats on water. Instead, it goes on land!

It is called a "stoneboat," and yet it is not made of stone, but of wood.

If you happen to live on a farm where there is a great deal of stony land, then you will know exactly what I mean; but in case you don't, perhaps I had better tell you.

A stoneboat is made of several heavy planks of wood stoutly nailed together and slightly curved at one end. It is really a sort of flat platform drawn by a horse, and used to carry away stones from the fields.

You see, where land is shallow and rocky, there is likely to be a number of big stones lying on or near the surface every spring, and the farmer likes to clear them away before he gets his plows to work. Sometimes the stoneboat is used in the opening up of new land, and then quite heavy boulders will be lifted on to it and hauled away.

Well, Leslie and Donovan were sent out with a stoneboat one day by their father, with orders to clear a certain field of stones.

The two boys rather enjoyed the job, and were soon working with a will. They liked to see the field gradually looking cleaner as they piled up the stones on the stoneboat and dumped them in a near-by dell. They felt that they were really helping father, and they knew how pleased he would be when the job was done.

47

All day long they worked out in the field, and by late afternoon they were feeling rather tired. It was almost time to quit and return home. Unexpectedly they came across a big and obstinate rock. It didn't look so big at first, for there was only a very little of it showing above the ground. But when they tried to move it, they found it was very large and was deeply buried.

Leslie took the crowbar they always carried with them for jobs like this and tried to lever it out. But it wouldn't move. They both got hold of the crowbar and heaved on it, but still the rock refused to budge.

"Oh, I'm too tired to move this one today," said Leslie. "Let's leave it. I won't have strength enough to play ball with the fellows this evening. Come on, let's go."

"All right," said Donovan. "We've picked up enough rocks anyway today. But what will father say if he sees this one left here?"

"Cover it over with earth, and then he won't see," said Leslie. "Then we'll come back tomorrow and take it away."

So they covered up the rock, and drove away with the last load on the stoneboat.

And, of course, they both forgot all about that rock. In fact, they did not think of it again until some days later, when father met them with a frown on his brow.

"Just broke my plow," he said. "Hit a rock up there in that field you two were supposed to have cleared."

Leslie and Donovan blushed as it all came back to their minds.

"Funny thing," said father, "that rock was only just under the surface. In fact, when I looked it over afterward it seemed to me that it had only recently been covered up."

The two boys looked away. There was nothing they could say.

By this time father had his suspicions; so he went on: "There is a text in the Bible which says, 'Be sure your sin will find you out.' And it seems to me that somebody's sin has been found out today."

Still the two boys remained silent.

"Well, boys," father continued, "I don't know what you did or didn't do, and it's too late now to alter things. But I want you to remember that those rocks are just like sins. Some can be picked up and got rid of without much trouble, but others are lodged deep down, with only a small part of them showing above the surface. You can't get rid of those by just covering them up. You have to dig them out, and the sooner the better. If you don't, there is always the chance that somebody will run into them and show them up; and if that doesn't happen, you can be dead sure that next year, after the winter rains, they will appear again as bare and ugly as ever. Deep-rooted sins must be dug out right away, as soon as they are found. And if you cannot move them with your own crowbar, you had better ask father to come and help."

"Thanks, dad," said the boys. "We understand, and we won't leave any rocks in the field next time."

Surely These Nice Dogs Wouldn't Bark at a Little Girl!

50

Saved From the Dogs

IT was in Pensacola, Florida, that I heard this interesting story, and this one, too, like so many of the others in this volume, came straight from the heart of a little child.

Barbara was only five years old at the time, but she was old enough to do all sorts of little jobs for her mother. She could dry the dishes, and wash them, too, when there was nothing *very* special to be done. She could sweep, and she could dust, and she could look after her baby brother as well—that is, when he was good. But most of all she loved to run errands.

Of course, mother did not let her go very far from home —just down to the near-by stores and across the road to the neighbors'. Mother had no worries about traffic, because there was little on the side street where they lived.

All the neighbors knew Barbara, and oftentimes, as they looked out of their windows, they would see her walking briskly along in her pretty little hat and coat; and they would say to themselves, "There's Barbara again. She must be going on another errand for her mother. What a good little girl she is!" And so, although she did not know it, Barbara was doing everyone good by just simply helping her mother, and doing what she was told.

Because nothing had ever gone wrong on any of her little journeys, Barbara knew no fear. She did not think that anything ever could go wrong. But then, one day, something happened.

51

It was evening, and mother wondered whether or not she should let Barbara go out so late, but as she needed some cheese and biscuits and other things for supper, she decided it would be all right. Surely, she thought, Barbara could easily run to the grocer's and back before dark. So she handed Barbara the money, repeated the order for the grocer, reminded her to come back quickly, and sent her away.

Barbara reached the store all right, and it was not long before she was out again and on her way home.

But she had not gone far from the store when she noticed two dogs following her. Perhaps they had smelled the biscuits, or the cheese, or something. Anyhow, they kept coming closer and closer, and were soon sniffing the bags in Barbara's hands.

"Go away, doggies!" she said, holding the bags high above her head.

But the dogs would not go away. Instead they began jumping up at the bags.

"Go away, go away, bad doggies!" she cried.

But they kept on jumping.

Barbara became a little frightened and started to run, but the dogs ran, too, and she could not get rid of them. They were barking now; and that made her still more frightened.

Seeing a short cut across a vacant lot, Barbara darted toward it, but, alas, two or three more dogs were playing there, and they came to join in the fun. By the time Barbara had reached the center of the vacant lot she was surrounded by seven or eight dogs. All were barking loudly and jumping up at her, trying to reach the sweet-smelling things in the bags.

Now Barbara, as I have told you, was only five years

old when this happened, just a dear, pretty little girl barely out of babyhood. But she had courage, and she had faith. And what do you suppose she did?

I know she did it, because she herself told me so, and she could not have been mistaken.

Well, with all those yapping, yelping dogs around her, she shut her eyes tight and prayed that Jesus would save her and make the dogs go away!

Suddenly all the yapping and the yelping ceased, and when Barbara opened her eyes, the dogs were all slinking away, with their tails between their legs, as though somebody had commanded them to go.

By this time mother was getting anxious about Barbara, and was out at the front gate, asking the neighbors whether they had seen her anywhere. But when Barbara came around the corner, and mother saw the beautiful look on her face, she knew that something unusual had happened. It had. Maybe it was just a little thing, but to Barbara it was something very, very wonderful, something she will never forget as long as she lives.

The Boat Came Back

A MOTHER and her young son, Bob, were out on a missionary journey near the mouth of a certain river that runs into the Gulf of Mexico. The mother was going from home to home, selling gospel literature, and Bob, well, he had just gone along to keep her company.

Early this particular morning they had crossed the river in a little boat and had then walked on some distance, calling at the few scattered homes they found, and seeking to interest the people in the things of God.

Then, alas, the weather changed. Dark, angry clouds rolled up, blotting out the sun, the wind rose to a gale, and the rain began to fall in torrents.

"We had better go home," said Bob, "or we'll be drenched."

"No," said mother, who wasn't one to turn back just because the weather was bad. "We'll wait in one of the houses awhile and see if it clears up."

It did clear up; so they went on again. Then it rained some more, and again they stood up under cover, going on again after that.

It was a hard day, especially for Bob. He couldn't understand why mother should want to continue her work under such conditions. He was tired and wet, and wished he hadn't come. After a while he began to say things to mother that he shouldn't have said.

At last mother decided that perhaps, after all, seeing

the weather was getting worse instead of better, they had better start for home. So, during a brief lull in the storm, they hurried back to the riverside, and found their boat safe and sound where they had left it.

"It looks rather rough out there," said mother, pointing to the whitecaps in the middle of the estuary, "but I suppose we shall be all right."

They took an oar apiece and began rowing, but it was terribly hard work, with the wind blowing in from the Gulf. And then, as they got farther and farther from the shore, the waves became so high that soon water was splashing over into the boat.

Mother became anxious.

"I think we had better turn around," she said. "It's too rough and dangerous out here. We shall have to wait for the wind to drop."

Bob agreed; so with heavy hearts they turned the boat round and headed back for the shore they had just left.

They reached it in safety, and Bob jumped out, mother following. She made a grab for the chain with which she planned to tie the boat up to a tree root on the shore, but her foot slipped on the soft, wet sand. As she staggered to get a new foothold, the boat slipped away, and, in less time than it takes to tell, it was drifting out on the tide!

"Look what you've done!" cried Bob angrily. "Why didn't you keep hold of the chain?"

Poor mother was overwhelmed with distress. Tired out, wet through, and worried about Bob, she had hoped so much to get back home early, but now their boat—their one means of getting back at all that night—was floating swiftly away from them.

There was nothing they could do now but just stand

there in the wind and rain, watching the boat grow smaller and smaller as it was swept ever farther away.

Bob continued to growl and mutter, blaming mother over and over again for letting the boat go like that. But suddenly he heard mother speaking to somebody—and it was not to him. He looked up, and there she was with her hands folded and her eyes tight shut.

"O Lord Jesus," she was praying, "you can see us here so tired and wet. We have been out working for you all day, and we want to get home. And now our boat has gone. I let it slip out of my hand, and what can we do? We can't reach it now, but you can. Won't you please bring our boat back to us?"

Bob was astonished. To think of his mother asking God to bring the boat back from the middle of that wind-swept estuary! It was foolish. It was unreasonable. Why, the boat would be far out in the Gulf in half an hour.

He looked out toward the boat. Then he began to stare at it.

"Mother," he said, "look! the boat has stopped moving. I am sure it has. Its position hasn't changed for two or three minutes. What can be holding it out there?"

Mother was staring at the boat now, with a light in her eyes that Bob had never seen before.

"Bob!" she cried, "the boat hasn't stopped. It is still moving; but it is coming this way!"

It was.

Slowly but surely it was moving back toward the shore from which it had drifted away, while mother and Bob stood there in awe and amazement, silently watching the most amazing sight of their lives.

Now it may have been the turning of the tide that caused

it, or the changing of the wind, or the ministry of an angel. I do not know. I cannot tell. But I do know—for this mother told me—that that little boat came gliding gently back to the very place from whence it had drifted away but a little while before. And it came so straight, she said, that it seemed to her that an unseen hand was guiding it.

By this time there was only a fresh breeze; so mother and Bob, with grateful hearts, stepped into the boat and rowed swiftly and happily homeward.

Bob was greatly impressed with what had happened, and nothing will ever change his belief that his mother's prayer was answered, and that their boat came sailing back to them with an angel at the helm.

58

Why Be Afraid of Shadows?

Never Afraid Again

"WHAT can be the matter with Joan?" mother said to herself as she went downstairs after putting her little girl to bed. "The poor child seems to be afraid to be left alone a single minute."

She settled herself comfortably in an armchair and picked up a book to read. But hardly had she read a paragraph before she heard Joan's voice calling again.

"Mamma, mamma!"

"What is it now, dear?" mother called back.

"Mamma, mamma, come here!" cried Joan, as though she was in terrible trouble.

Mother left her chair and began climbing the stairs.

"Now what is it, Joan?" she asked, as she came up.

"You turned the light out in the hall," cried Joan, "and it's all dark in here."

"I'm sorry," said mother. "I'll turn it on again; but go to sleep, dear. It doesn't really matter whether it is dark or light if we love Jesus. There's no reason to be afraid of the dark."

"I know," said Joan, "but please turn on the light."

Mother turned on the hall light, kissed Joan good night once more, and went downstairs again to her comfortable chair and her book.

But there was to be no rest for mamma this night, and certainly no reading of her book. A few moments later she heard Joan again.

59

"Mamma, mamma!"

"Oh, Joan, what is it now?" she called.

"Mamma, come quick, come quick!"

Mother dropped her book and climbed the stairs again.

"Joan, dear," she said, as she went into the bedroom, "what is the matter with you? Why don't you go to sleep? All the other boys and girls in the whole town are fast asleep by now."

"Mamma," cried Joan, shaking all over with fear, "look over there."

"Over where?" asked mother.

"Over there by the chimney. I'm sure I saw a hobgoblin there, and it came walking over toward my bed."

"Hobgoblin fiddlesticks!" cried mother. "There isn't such a thing as a hobgoblin, and never was. Who has been telling you such foolish stories?"

"Ah, but there are hobgoblins," said Joan solemnly. "Eva May told me."

"Eva May!" exclaimed mother in great indignation. "A little girl of nine telling you such things! Just wait till I see her mother. But what else did she tell you?"

"She said that if I wasn't a good girl, the hobgoblins would come down the chimney at night and get me."

"How stupid!" cried mother. "And what else?"

"She told me that maybe a great big bear would crawl in through the window in the dark and creep under my bed and gobble me up before the morning."

"But there isn't a bear within a hundred miles, Joan," cried mother. "And how could a bear climb up this house and get in that window? It is all too silly for words."

But Joan wasn't quite sure about it. Who was right? Mother or Eva May? Her friend was such a big girl, and she seemed to know everything.   So for a moment Joan was quiet, thinking it over.

"Now, Joan," said mother, "try not to think of these things again.   They are not true and couldn't be true; and it is foolish to fear things that don't exist.   Why be afraid of shadows?"

Joan, still pale and trembling, put her curly head down on the pillow again.

"I wish they wouldn't come here any more," she said.

"They won't," said mother, gently stroking the poor, troubled little head.   "Don't worry any more, dear.   And if you are afraid again, just tell Jesus about it.   And remember, Joan, you have a guardian angel, too.   Jesus has told him to watch over you, and he won't let any horrid things come near you at night."

"I know," said Joan.   "I have told Jesus about it over and over again, but somehow it doesn't make any difference. I still seem to see them coming to me."

"Well, Joan dear, tell Him again.   Indeed, we will both tell Him now."

So mother prayed a beautiful prayer, asking Jesus to protect little Joan from all harm and danger, and to help her forget the foolish stories she had heard.   She prayed, too, that Joan might realize that her guardian angel was near at hand at all times, in the daytime and in the night; and that she might learn to trust and not be afraid.

Just then the telephone rang, and mother went downstairs to answer it.   By and by she came to the bottom of the stairs and called up to Joan.

"Mrs. Jones wants me to come over to see her for a few minutes; she says it's very important.   Will you be all right while I go?   I won't be very long."

"All right," called Joan. "But don't be long, mamma, will you?"

"No," called mother. "I'll be back in just a minute."

Then silence fell in the house, and Joan lay in her little bed, still thinking over all that her mother had said; and every time the old, ugly thoughts tried to come back, she would pray ever so hard and try to believe that everything was really all right.

And then something very wonderful happened. (I know it happened because not only did Joan's mother tell me about it, but Joan herself wrote and described it all, and I have her letter beside me as I write.)

Suddenly a beautiful light shone in the room, and Joan saw a glorious being standing close by her bed. A lovely face smiled down at her, as though saying to her, "Little girl, don't be afraid."

For an instant Joan became cold with fear, but as she looked at that shining figure, so radiant and so kindly, a wonderful peace and quietness came over her little soul.

It was all over in a very little while, and soon the light had faded and the glorious being had vanished from sight. But from that moment everything was different.

Not long after that, mother returned. As soon as she entered the house she heard Joan calling her.

"Mamma, mamma!"

But there was a new note in Joan's voice. Mother noticed it at once. This was not the voice of someone afraid, but of someone with joy and gladness in her heart.

"Mamma!" cried Joan, as mother entered the room, "Jesus has been here, or my guardian angel. Really, mamma. He stood just there, close to my bed."

And then Joan told mother all about the glorious being she had seen and the beautiful light that had shone in her room. And mother knew from the look on Joan's face, all aglow with happiness, that what she said was true.

Joan is not a little girl any more. She is grown up now. But not for a single moment has she forgotten what happened on that wonderful night long, long ago, when she was only five years old. All her life she has loved Jesus, and, as she told me herself, she was never afraid again.

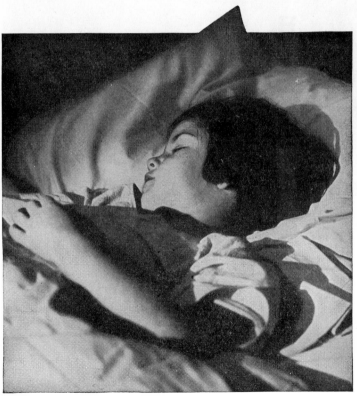

H. A. Roberts

No Further Fears—Joan Sleeps Peacefully

Up in the Almond Tree

64

Steve's Self-Starter

O N the whole Steve was really a very good little boy,
but there was one important thing he seemed to lack,
and that was a self-starter.

Perhaps it isn't right to suggest that he didn't have one
at all, for when there was a game being played in which he
wanted to join, why, he would start off at a run without
the slightest difficulty. Likewise when mother told him he
could go to the corner store and buy some candy, he would
speed away like a streak of lightning. But if mother said,
"Steve, I wish you would bring in some wood for the fire,"
or if father said, "Steve, run and post these letters for me,"
well, Steve's self-starter just went right out of action.

Both father and mother came to notice that whenever
Steve wanted to do something to please himself, he could do
it very quickly; there was no waiting at all; but whenever
Steve was asked to do something to please somebody else,
he would find all sorts of excuses for not doing it.

Perhaps you may know some other little boy or some
little girl who behaves like this. I wonder!

Well, Steve's mother and father didn't like it at all, and
they began to talk over together how they might get Steve's
self-starter into proper working order.

One day toward the end of the summer father decided
that the time had come to gather the nuts off the big almond
tree in the garden. Already some of the almonds had
fallen to the ground, and the outer shells of most of the

65

others were already cracking, which is a sure sign that harvesttime has arrived.

This seemed like an easy little job for Steve. All he had to do was to take a long stick, knock the almonds off the tree, and then pick them up and put them in a bucket. Father felt sure that he would love to do it. But in this father was sadly mistaken. Once more Steve's self-starter failed to act.

Now, if father had asked him to climb the tree, well, that would have been different. Steve liked climbing trees, but he didn't like picking nuts. So, before long, instead of doing the job, he wandered off to play with the little boy next door, and completely forgot all about the almond tree.

When father came home from work that evening, the first question he asked was about the almonds. How many pounds had Steve picked? Well, he hadn't picked any. He had been very busy all day, of course, but not picking almonds. He had ridden his bicycle a good deal, he had had a great deal of fun in various ways, but, well, he hadn't picked the nuts. In fact, he didn't like picking nuts.

"Now look here, Steve," said father, "I am just about tired of this. When I ask you to pick nuts, I expect you to pick them, and not run off next door or somewhere else. Don't you realize, too, that if you don't pick those nuts right away, then the squirrels will get them, and there won't be any for us? They have probably taken scores of them already. So get that self-starter of yours working tomorrow, or I don't know what I'll do about it. Maybe I'll have to take the stick you should have used on the tree and use it somewhere else."

At this point father went off to talk to mother, and Steve overheard him saying something about sparing the rod and spoiling the child. He began to wonder if the time hadn't come to obey a little more promptly than he had been doing of late. And then, too, he didn't like to think that perhaps the squirrels would beat him to the job of picking those nuts.

The next morning, very early, while father and mother were still in bed, there was a big bang on their bedroom door. They both jumped up suddenly, wondering whatever could be the matter. A moment later the door flew open, and in rushed Steve, his face wreathed in smiles and in his two little hands the biggest bucket he could find.

"They're all picked!" he cried, excitedly. "I got up at five o'clock to pick them!"

The bucket was nearly full of almonds.

Steve's self-starter had worked at last.

Her Sabbath Socks

I WISH you could meet Carol. She is the sweetest little thing, just about seven years old.

We had a delightful chat together, and she told me this story about her socks.

Her mother had given her a beautiful new blue dress and some new blue socks to go with it. Carol was very much pleased that they matched so well.

Mother's idea, of course, was that Carol should wear these pretty new clothes the very next time she went to church, and Carol was delighted at the idea. She could hardly wait for the Sabbath day to come. She was very anxious to wear that new dress and those new socks.

Sabbath came at last, and Carol was up bright and early, hoping to put on the new dress right way, but mother said that she had to wait until just before church time, so that she wouldn't crease it, or spill anything on it.

Those last few hours seemed like days and weeks, they passed so slowly. But at last mother said, "It's time to get dressed for church, Carol," and Carol never ran to mother more quickly in all her life.

What a beautiful dress it was! Carol's eyes sparkled as mother gently lifted it from its hook in the closet.

"And now the socks, mother," she said, happily.

The socks! Alas, they were nowhere to be found.

"But where can they be?" asked Carol.

"I don't know," said mother, searching feverishly. "I

68

am sure they were right here only yesterday evening. What could have happened to them?"

"Oh, do hurry up and find them," said Carol. "It's almost time to go."

"I'm hurrying as much as I can," said mother. "You must look as well."

"I am looking," said Carol, as she peered under the bed and in the cupboard and everywhere else where she thought the socks might be.

Five minutes passed, ten minutes. Church time was near—so near that mother didn't dare look at the clock. And still the socks could not be found. Poor mother was almost in a panic, and Carol was on the point of tears.

"Perhaps you had better put on another pair, after all," said mother. "I'm so sorry, but—"

"Oh, no," cried Carol. "I mustn't do that. Surely we can find the new ones. They match the dress so beautifully. Mother, shall we ask Jesus to help us find them?"

Mother stopped looking for the socks and turned to look at Carol. She saw in her eyes the simple faith of a little child. "All right, dear," she said, "let's."

So there and then, rushed and troubled as they were, they knelt by Carol's little bed and rolled their burden on the Lord.

"Please, dear Jesus," prayed Carol, "show us where my new socks have gone."

A moment later they were both on their feet again. There was no time to lose.

"I think I will take another look in your top drawer," said mother.

She looked again, and there they were!

H. M. Lambert

Looking Up to Heaven

Jesus Told Her

THE little girl in this story was only three years old when she did this lovely thing I am going to tell you about. What a great deal of good even a tiny three-year-old can do!

Her father is an important businessman, a very important one, but not so long ago he became very, very ill. He was so sick that two doctors were called in, and the servants in the great big house where he lived were told to go about their work without making the least little bit of noise, so that the master would not be disturbed.

Nobody was allowed in the sickroom except the nurse and the doctors. They were most particular about this. There was to be no troubling of the patient for any reason whatever, they said. If he did not sleep, then there would be no hope of saving his life.

And that was just what the patient could not do. Sleep would not come. Hour after hour he tossed about, restless and irritable, and constantly getting weaker.

As the days passed and he became steadily worse, the doctors finally decided that there was nothing more that they could do. It was only a matter of time, they said, and the family had better prepare for the worst.

All this time little Gloria had been consumed with curiosity regarding what was going on in the darkened room. She knew her dear daddy was sick in there, but she couldn't understand why she was not allowed to go in, why she had to be kept so far away from him.

Now and then, when nobody was looking, she would creep along to the door of the sickroom and stand outside listening, as quiet as a little pussy hunting a mouse. There she would stay until the nurse opened the door, and then she would run away so fast that there was no time for the nurse to blame her for being there.

How little Gloria did want to see her daddy! She felt that he needed her, and it made her so cross to be told that she mustn't go in his room any more.

Then one afternoon, as she was looking around a corner of the corridor, sadly watching the door of daddy's room, the nurse came out and walked down to the bathroom. And she left the door open!

Like a streak of lightning Gloria sped around the corner and into the room. She just *had* to see her daddy, and I couldn't blame her very much, could you?

But when she saw her daddy, she felt very sad. He looked so pale and tired.

"Poor daddy!" she said, gently touching his hand. "I'm so sorry." And then after a pause, "I love you, daddy."

Daddy turned his head and smiled weakly at her. "I'm glad you came to see me," he whispered, trying to stroke her golden curls.

Tears filled Gloria's eyes, and all of a sudden she walked over to the window and looked up into the sky. And there she talked quietly to Jesus, just as though she were talking to a very dear friend. In a moment or two she was back again at her daddy's bedside.

"Daddy," she said very earnestly, with her sweet little face aglow with happiness, "Jesus told me just now that you are going to get better."

Daddy smiled and slowly closed his eyes.

Just then Gloria heard footsteps. It was the nurse coming back! But Gloria didn't even think of running to hide. It was her turn now.

"Ssssh!" she said, as the nurse came in, an angry frown on her face. "Ssssh! my daddy's asleep. Don't wake him up."

The nurse looked, and to her amazement she saw that Gloria was right. Her patient was asleep at last. The little girl had done more than all the doctors and the nurses together.

The poor sick man, whom everybody had given up to die, slept soundly all that night, something he had not done for many weeks. In the morning, when he awoke, he was so much better that the doctors could hardly believe their eyes. And he kept on getting better until soon he was his old self again.

Today he is back at his work, but he never tires of telling the story of how his life was saved, not by the doctors, but by his own little Gloria and the prayer she prayed at the window that afternoon.

Held Up by a Robin

YES, it was a whole railroad system that was held up, and by a little robin redbreast, too!

Two little girls told me the story, and I am sure it must be true, for it all happened close by the town where they live. And, from what they said, everybody was talking about it for weeks.

It all began one afternoon when a freight train was slowly steaming out of the station. It had not traveled very far when the brakeman noticed that a little robin was flying alongside the train.

"Look at that bird!" he said to a man who was with him. "It's following us."

"So it is! It seems to be trying to get underneath this caboose. But I suppose it will fly off soon."

But the bird kept flying close to the caboose, and as the train gathered speed, it flew faster and faster. After a while, however, the pace became too swift for it, and the poor little bird had to give up. It flew off and perched on a tree, gradually becoming smaller and smaller as the train steamed on, until at last it was out of sight.

Why the brakeman should bother about one little robin redbreast I don't know, but perhaps it was because the bird looked so sad as it gave up the race and perched on the tree. Anyhow, as soon as the train stopped at the next station he jumped down and looked underneath the caboose. And what do you suppose he found there? Away underneath in

74

a corner was a robin's nest, with three pale-blue eggs in it!

Now he knew why the poor little bird had been flying so fast! But where was Mrs. Redbreast now? he wondered. Could she have followed?

He held up the train as long as he dared, hoping she would catch up in time to get back to her nest, but she did not come. At last he had to give the signal to go, but before doing so he walked up to the engine and chatted with the driver, telling him all about the nest, and particularly about the eggs.

Now the driver of that freight train had just as kind a heart as the brakeman; so he promised to drive with special care, so that the eggs would not be jolted out of the nest. And how gently he brought that train to a stop every time! If he had had the President on board he couldn't have done it better.

So the train ran all the way to its destination and all the way back again. And at every stop the brakeman got out and looked underneath to make sure the eggs were there.

At last the return journey had been made, and the train was back in the home station. But where was the mother bird that had last been seen perched on the branch of a tree many miles out along the railroad line?

She was not far away. Indeed, even as the brakeman stood looking underneath once more, there was a sudden fluttering of wings, and faithful Mrs. Redbreast dived under the caboose and sat on her nest again.

But now what to do? Of course the brakeman could have forgotten all about it, but he didn't. Having taken so much care of those eggs all day long, he felt a special interest in them now. So he told the stationmaster what had happened, and he came over to see the robin.

The stationmaster said that the best thing to do would be to disconnect the caboose and shunt it onto a siding until the eggs were hatched. You see, he had a kind heart, too, as big as that of the driver and the brakeman. But the trouble was that, to do anything like this, he had to get permission from the head office of the railroad; and what excuse could he give for holding up the caboose? Furthermore, there was another difficulty. This was the only caboose available for this particular train, and how could they get another one before this train had to leave the next day? Would the head office be willing to send another caboose all the way down the line just because a robin was sitting on a nest? Not very likely, thought the stationmaster. But, being such a kind-hearted man, and anxious to help the poor little bird if he could, he decided to phone the head office and ask. They could but refuse.

Now it so happened that, by this time, the news about the robin's nest under the caboose had spread all through the town. The brakeman had talked about it and the engineer had talked about it; and then their wives and their children began to talk about it, until the whole town became excited, and people by the hundred were streaming down to the station to see this unusual sight.

As you can imagine, when so many men and women and boys and girls were all running to one place, the newspaper men became interested, too, and they ran down there with their pens and their notebooks and their cameras and what not. So, within a very short time the news of Mrs. Red-breast's adventure was on the front pages of the local papers.

News like this travels fast. In fact, it reached the head office of the railroad before the stationmaster was able to speak to the man he wanted on the telephone. By great good fortune, this proved to be another man with a heart as big and kind as that of the stationmaster, the brakeman, or the engineer. So when the stationmaster asked if he could have another caboose, so that Mrs. Robin should not be disturbed, the official replied, "Of course! That caboose is not to be moved under any condition until the eggs have been hatched."

The next day another caboose arrived just in time for the train.

Well, Mrs. Robin sat there on her nest day after day like a little queen on her throne, smiling—that is, if robins do smile—at all the hundreds of children and grownups who came to look at her. And then one great day the eggs were hatched and the proud mother began feeding her little brood. Orders then came from the head office that the caboose was not to be moved until all the baby birds had been taught to fly and had left the nest. So the little family stayed on as guests of the railroad until they decided to go somewhere else.

And now, just think of those four men upsetting the program of a railroad for the sake of one little bird! What a lot of kindhearted people there still are in this sad old world! And how much simple joy their thoughtfulness for one of God's smallest creatures brought into the lives of hundreds of their fellow men!

H. M. Lambert

It Was in Covered Wagons Such as This, but Usually Drawn by Oxen, That Pioneers Crossed America a Hundred Years Ago

78

The Mysterious Rider

ARE you lucky enough to have a grandma? If so, then, the first chance you get, ask her to tell you some of the things that happened to her when she was a little girl. I wouldn't be surprised if they prove to be the most interesting stories you have heard.

Grandma McAlpine was like that. Although she was nearly eighty years of age, she could remember almost everything about her childhood; and how her grandchildren did love to listen to her!

One evening Frank and Bessie were visiting in her home, and soon they were trying to persuade her to tell them one of her grand old stories of the long ago.

"Please, grandma!" urged Bessie. "Just one. We love to listen to your stories."

"Do, please!" chimed in Frank. "You know, grandma, that one you promised to tell us, about the mysterious rider."

A smile came over grandma's face.

"All right then," said grandma. "Make yourselves comfortable, and I'll tell you now."

Frank and Bessie seated themselves as close to grandma as possible, and looked up expectantly into her face, knowing that a rare treat was in store for them.

"It was nearly seventy-five years ago this October," grandma began, "when I was a little girl of five, but I remember it all as clearly as if it had happened yesterday.

79

"But to begin my story I must go back farther still," continued grandma. "A hundred years or so before that, my great-grandfather left the old country and set sail with his family for America. They settled in New England, and the children grew up and moved onto farms of their own. Into one of those families my father was born, and when he was only a young man he heard people talking about a great wonderland in the West.

"Away out toward the sunset, it was said, there were thousands and thousands of square miles of marvelous forests where grew the greatest trees that man had ever seen. The soil was so rich that it would grow finer wheat than any farmer had ever raised. In fact, there was everything there that the heart of man could desire.

"My father listened. It seemed promising to him. It was just what he wanted. So he talked to my mother, and finally they decided to go.

"There were no trains then, and no roads. It meant a journey of three thousand miles across open prairies, through forests and rivers and over mountain chains. And all their goods had to be crowded into one old covered wagon, drawn by two oxen."

"Tell us about the covered wagon," said Bessie.

"Well, just a word," said grandma, "for we haven't got to the real story yet. Most of the covered wagons were built of strong, thick planks. They were made long and narrow, so that they could be used as boats in crossing rivers.

"Usually several families traveled together, not only for company, but to guard against Indians, who often attacked these caravans. They thought the white people were coming to drive them off their lands."

"And did you travel in one of those covered wagons?" asked Bessie, her eyes wide open with wonder.

"Yes, I surely did," said grandma. "I was only five when we started out, but I can still see everything that happened on that long, long journey."

"How long did it take?" asked Frank.

"More than six months," said grandma. "We left our home in April, as soon as the snow was gone, and it was October before we caught sight of Mt. Hood in Oregon, away over in the West. There were seven or eight other wagons in our caravan, and day by day we moved slowly on, just as fast as the oxen would take us.

"Some days it was very, very hot, and then we would all get terribly thirsty. I think the oxen felt it more than we did, because they had most of the work to do. I remember one day we had traveled many miles without water. Suddenly the oxen stopped. They refused to haul the wagon another yard. Father took the yokes off them, and suddenly they started to run. They had either seen or scented water more than a mile away, but they were too weary to take the wagon with them."

"Did you catch them?" asked Frank.

"Oh, yes," said grandma. "That was easy. They only wanted to drink. Then we started off again."

"But the rider—the mysterious rider—when did he appear?" asked Bessie.

"Just you wait a minute," said grandma. "We're coming to that all in good time. Some other things were to happen first. As we rode on day after day, week after week, month after month, the poor oxen became more and more footsore and weary. Father did not dare to let them rest very much, for he knew that he had to get over the mountains before the snow should fall. Then, too, the food began to give out. We were allowed just so much a day, and no more, for father said that if we were delayed and ran out of food, we should die on the way.

"And so, with the oxen becoming more and more tired, and father getting more and more worried, we moved on westward. At long last we started to climb the Cascade Mountains. I can't think how anyone ever found a way across, for there were no beautiful roads as there are nowadays, and it was all so wild and rocky that we were nearly jolted out of the wagon many a time. Still we went on, climbing up and up, with the oxen panting and sweating in front, and father shoving his hardest behind.

"At last we reached the summit, and in the distance we could see Mt. Hood, its white peak gleaming in the morning sun. We knew that there would still be many more days of travel; yet it seemed to us then that the journey was almost over.

"And then, that very morning, one of our oxen died. The climb up the mountains had been too much for it. We were left with one ox; and one could never pull that heavy wagon. Father was at his wit's end to know what to do. He talked to the people in the other wagons. They were sorry, but they could not do anything. Their oxen, too, were almost worn out, and their food was almost gone. They felt that they had to go on without us. And so they did.

"I shall never forget how we all felt when the last wagon had gone out of sight down the steep, rough trail. There we were, alone on the summit of the Cascade Mountains, with no means of getting away, and only enough food to last us two or three days.

"Night came on. It was very cold. Father wondered whether the snow would come, and what we would do then. He kindled a fire and gave us something to eat, and then I was put to bed. But he and mother sat up and talked of what they could do.

"By and by father said to mother, 'Surely the great God who has brought us in safety all this long way, through so many troubles, will not desert us now. Let us kneel here on the mountaintop and tell Him of our plight.' And there they knelt, the two of them, in the dark, with the cold wind blowing around them, as they told God all that had happened, and how they trusted Him to deliver them. Then they arose, and soon after that they tried to sleep.

"The night wore on. Upon our little, lonely camp the bright, cold stars looked down. Midnight passed, one o'clock, two o'clock, three o'clock. Dawn was just beginning to break when father sat up. The silence had been broken by strange sounds.

"Clippety-clop, clippety-clop, clippety-clop.

" 'Horses!' whispered father.

" 'Do you think it's Indians?' whispered mother, leaping to his side.

" 'I don't know, said father. 'We must wait and see.'

"They stood quietly beside the wagon, listening and watching as the sound of the horses' hoofs came ever nearer and nearer.

"Suddenly out of the darkness came a voice.

" 'Hi there!' cried someone.

" 'Who is it?' called father.

" 'A friend,' was the answer.

"In the dim morning light father could just make out the form of a man on horseback, with another horse beside him. He immediately walked over toward the stranger

" 'Are you in trouble?' asked the mysterious rider.

" 'We are,' said father, 'desperate trouble. One of our oxen has died, and we are stranded here with scarcely any food left.'

"Then the stranger told his story. 'At two o'clock this morning,' he said, 'I was suddenly awakened, and a voice seemed to say to me, "There is someone in trouble on the mountains; go and help him." So I got up at once, saddled my two horses, and started off. I was determined not to stop until I found the one who needed help. What can I do for you?'

"The mysterious rider took us to his own home and fed us. Then he lent us another ox, so that we were able to reach the end of our journey in safety."

"What was the name of the mysterious rider?" asked Frank.

"He never told us," said grandma. "He just said we were to call him the Colonel, which we have done ever since."

"But who gave him the message that you were in trouble?" asked Bessie.

"Ah," said grandma, "that is the most wonderful part of the story, for there was no telephone in those days and no telegraph. All father could do was to tell God, and God did all the rest.

"All my life," she added, "I have never forgotten that terrible night on the mountains, when God sent the mysterious rider to our rescue. And, children, I want you ever to remember that the great God whom we love and serve never forgets His own. 'The God of Jacob is our refuge.' 'Blessed are all they that put their trust in Him.' "

Lost in the Rain

HAVE you ever been lost? If not, you can hardly imagine what a terrible experience it is.

Perhaps you have wondered sometimes just what you would do if ever you were to be lost. Well, Amy and her sister Ruby did get lost one day, and I am sure you will want to know what happened to them.

Just how old they were at the time I am not sure. I should say that Ruby was not more than five, and Amy about eight. Of course, Amy, being three years older than Ruby felt that she was nearly grown up, and was well able to take care of her little sister.

Both of them loved flowers, and having heard that there were some beautiful primroses in the woods, they decided that they would go and pick some for mother.

As the woods were not very far away from their house, they thought they would not be gone very long; so they did not tell anybody they were going; and then, too, they wanted to surprise mother with the flowers.

So away they went, hand in hand.

Soon they were romping happily through the trees, but as the undergrowth became thicker and thicker, they had to walk single file along the narrow, winding path. On and on they went, keeping their eyes open for the clusters of primroses that they had been told were now in bloom. They saw a few here and there, but they continued to walk farther

85

and farther into the woods, in the hope of finding still better and bigger flowers.

So glad were they to be going flower picking all on their own that they did not notice how far they had traveled, or how the time was passing. Neither did they notice that the weather was changing. But it was.

By and by, when they had gone at least two miles, Ruby looked up through the trees. "How dark it is getting," she said.

"So it is, Ruby," said Amy. "I didn't notice it before. What big black clouds are up in the sky! And it's beginning to rain. Feel it, Ruby."

Ruby stretched out her chubby little hand to catch the raindrops.

Just then there was a bright flash of lightning, followed by a loud peal of thunder.

"Oh!" they cried together, taking tight hold of each other's hands.

"There's going to be a storm," said Amy.

"I don't like storms," cried Ruby. "They make me frightened."

There was another bright flash, another boom of thunder, and then the wind roared through the woods, swaying the trees in a terrifying way. A moment later down came the rain.

How it rained! Ruby didn't try to catch it now. It caught her, and Amy, too, until it had soaked their hair, their dresses, their socks, their shoes.

"We must hurry back home!" cried Amy, very much frightened. "Run! Ruby, run!"

They ran, splashing through the mud, with Amy in front and Ruby following as best she could behind.

For five minutes or more they ran, with the rain beating down on them and the thunder crashing overhead. Then Amy stopped.

"Where are we?" she cried, alarmed. "We're lost! I've forgotten which path we came on. Oh, what shall we do? What shall we do?"

Then they both began to cry, too, their tears chasing the raindrops down their cheeks.

For two or three minutes they stood there sobbing. Then Ruby remembered something she had learned from mother.

"Amy," she said to her big sister, "mamma said once that if ever we got into trouble, we should tell God about it and ask Him to help us. Do you think we should ask Him now?"

"Perhaps we should," said Amy. "If we were to kneel down here and tell Him we're lost, maybe He would do something for us."

So then and there those two dear little girls, soaked to the skin and shivering with cold, knelt down in the mud, with the rain streaming down their bowed heads, and asked God to help them find their way out of the woods.

As they rose to their feet Amy pointed to a certain crooked tree some distance away.

"Look, Ruby," she said. "Isn't that the funny-looking tree we saw some time ago when we came into the woods?"

Ruby thought it was, and the two hurried over to it. There, by that crooked tree, they found the very path that they wanted, the one that led out of the woods. Soon they were both home again, getting dry and warm beside the fire.

"Mamma," said Ruby, with a lovely light in her bright blue eyes, "we never would have got back if Jesus hadn't shown us the way."

Mother's Mittens

THERE was considerable commotion upstairs, and mother began to wonder what it was all about.

Milly was supposed to be getting ready for school, but instead there was a loud banging and slamming of doors and drawers, and some shouting that did not sound very polite.

"What is the matter, Milly?" mother called. "You'll be late for school again if you don't hurry."

Milly appeared at the top of the stairs, all hot and bothered. "I can't find my mittens," she said. "I've searched everywhere. Somebody must have taken them— or they're lost. Oh, dear!"

And with that, mittenless, Milly swept downstairs and out of the front door, just in time to catch the bus for school.

"The careless little miss!" said mother, as she closed the door. "That's the third pair she has lost this year. And what a fuss to make! I think I'll have to tell her about my mother's mittens tonight, and see if that will help."

So when Milly returned that afternoon, mother took the first opportunity to suggest a story, and Milly, who loved stories, was perfectly ready to listen.

"I would like to tell you something about my mother," she began. "It's a story she once told me, which I have never forgotten. When she was a very little girl, she lived on a farm. Her family were very poor, and everybody, from the youngest to the oldest, was expected to work, and work

hard. Her father was a very strict man, and believed that
the only way to bring up children was to punish them fre-
quently. Little Mary—my mother—came to be dreadfully
afraid of him. She knew that if she did anything wrong,
she would be sure to get a good beating.

"One day, when she was still only a very small girl, she
was sent out to mind the sheep. Yes, and she had to take
her three-year-old sister along with her as well!

"The weather was cold, and little Mary was so thankful to have a pair of nice warm mittens her mother had
knit for her."

"Mittens!" said Milly. "So she had mittens, too?"

"Yes, she had," said mother. "And I want you to hear
what happened to them—and to poor Mary. She spent
all that cold day in the heather with the sheep, and then, as
evening drew on, she drove the sheep back to the farmyard.
Carefully she counted them over and over again, for she
knew just what to expect from her father if she arrived with
one missing.

"At last she drew near the house. There was a light
in the kitchen and the warm glow of a large wood fire. How
cheerful it looked! How happy she would be to get into
the warm again! She reached the door. It opened, and
there stood her father. He let little sister go in, but looked
sternly at Mary. He had no thanks for her. Suddenly
he noticed that one mitten was missing.

" 'What does this mean?' he asked gruffly. 'That mitten must be found tonight, before you come indoors. Other-
wise you will be thrashed.' "

"Thrashed for losing a mitten!" exclaimed Milly.

"Yes," said mother, "and the poor little thing had to go
out into the freezing farmyard again and try to find the

mitten. But how could she find it? She had been walking about all day with the sheep, and it might be lying anywhere in the vast expanse of heather. Where could it be? Oh, how she did wish she could go back into the warm kitchen! But she knew that she did not dare to do that. She had to stay outside until the mitten was found.

"At last, as she was shivering, she decided to go into the pigpen. She knew it wouldn't be so cold in there. She could get a little warmth from the pigs. And it was while she was there that she suddenly thought about God. Maybe the pigs brought back to her mind the story of the prodigal son. I don't know. But there and then she dropped to her knees and poured out her sorrow to the Lord. She told Him that she had worked hard all day, that she had tried to be good, that she had cared for baby sister, and that she hadn't meant to lose the mitten. It had just got lost, and she didn't know where to find it. Would God please help her find it, because she was so cold and so dreadfully hungry, and she did so want to go back into the warm kitchen."

"Poor little thing," said Milly, "and all over a mitten!"

"Yes," said mother, "all over a mitten. But, Milly, what do you suppose happened when Mary rose to her feet and walked out of the pigpen?"

"I couldn't guess," said Milly.

"Well, she kicked something soft with her foot, and, looking down, there was the missing mitten! She picked it up, ran to the kitchen door, and was welcomed in at last."

"But why did you tell me that story?" asked Milly.

"Can't you guess?" said mother. "Don't you remember the terrible fuss you made this morning, and how you finally ran off to school in a very bad temper, all over a mitten?"

"Well, it was enough to upset anybody," said Milly, and then, after a pause, "You don't mean that I should ask God to help me find a mitten, do you? That might have happened long ago, when your mother was a little girl, but—"

"But, Milly," said mother, "God does not change. He is the same yesterday, today, and forever. And the same God who helped my mother find a lost mitten can still help my little girl today. And when we ask Him to help us in the little things of life, it takes all the burden away, and there's no more fretting and banging and shouting. We just leave it to the Lord, and all is well."

"Well, maybe I'll try it next time," said Milly.

"I know it will help," said mother. "We may not always find the things we lose just when we ask for them; sometimes God sees that it is best to delay the answers to our prayers; but I do know this, that just telling Him about our troubles does us a great deal of good."

H. A. Roberts

The Cold, Gray Sea

92

Holding His Hand

THERE were three hundred children on the ship at the time, three hundred boys and girls with smiles on their faces and a great ache deep down in their hearts.

You see, all of them had just said good-by to fathers and mothers, perhaps not to see them again until after the war, whenever that might be.

Of course they were going to be brave; that was why they were smiling; but they couldn't help thinking of the dear ones they had left behind; maybe of their baby sisters and brothers and their pet dogs and cats and all the things that make home dear.

And now they were leaving the land they knew and loved so well, and setting sail for a foreign country, knowing only that there would be kind friends there and a warm welcome—that is, if they got through all right.

There was another worry. Would they get through? Another big ship crowded with children had just been sunk, and some had been drowned despite all that the gallant sailors could do to help them. Perhaps there would be another submarine about this time, or a dive bomber. Maybe. But they had promised to be brave, and they would be, come what might.

The first day out all the passengers on the ship, from the youngest to the oldest, were lined up on deck to be told what to do if any "emergency" should arise. In the front row were the three hundred children, behind them the women passengers, and behind them again, the men. When they were all assembled, one of the chief officers began to explain about the lifeboats, and who was to go in each of them if they should be attacked. Then he told about the rafts, and how to hold on to them. After that he took a lifesaving jacket and showed them how that should be worn, pointing out how important it was that it should be tied on in just the right way. Then he took a life belt and let everyone see exactly how one should put it over his head that he might be supported while swimming about in the sea.

Among the hundreds of people on the deck at this time was little Tommy. He was only six years old, hardly old enough, indeed, to know what it was all about. Among all these children and grownups he didn't know a single soul, and he felt very, very lonely. If only he could see his mother again, just for a minute!

Tommy kept his eyes glued on the man with the stripes on his arm and the gold buttons on his coat. What was he saying?

"Now if we should be torpedoed, which we hope won't happen, then all you children over here make at once for this lifeboat."

It seemed to Tommy as though the man with the gold buttons was pointing right at him; so he looked up at the lifeboat and wondered why he should have to get in that little boat. It didn't look safe; it was so small beside the big steamer.

"And if there isn't time to get to the lifeboat," went on the big man with the bright-gold buttons, "then grab a life belt if you can, and jump into the sea."

Jump into the sea! thought Tommy. How dreadful!

Just then the ship rolled, and Tommy could see the great expanse of the ocean, so cold and gray and unfriendly that it made his poor little heart sadder than ever, and frightened, too.

Does he mean that I have to jump over into the sea? he asked himself, and he didn't like to answer it. And, of course, he couldn't ask anybody else, because he might think he was afraid, and he had promised mother he would be brave.

Soon the officer said, "That's all for now, and don't forget to keep your life jackets on till we have passed the danger zone," and with that they were all dismissed like a class at school.

Some went back to their cabins and some to the dining room, and soon Tommy found he was all by himself. Making sure that nobody was looking, he picked up a life belt and quietly carried it downstairs.

Not knowing what else to do, he sat down on the bottom stair and waited all alone, his arm through the life belt.

How long he sat there I do not know, but by and by a man came along and spoke to him. Tommy recognized him as one of the teachers who had come on the boat to care for the children.

"Hello, Tommy!" he cried. "What are you doing here all by yourself?"

Tommy looked up with a strange sadness on his little face.

"Please, sir," he asked, "how do I put this on?"

"I'll show you," said the teacher, kindly. "First you do this. Then you do that. See? It's quite easy, isn't it?"

"Yes," said Tommy. "Thank you. I see. But, please sir, I don't want to jump into the sea."

Tears came into the teacher's eyes, but he didn't dare let Tommy know how he was feeling, for he had to be brave, too.

"Oh," he said cheerfully, "you won't have to jump into the sea. Of course not. Everything is going to be all right. You'll see."

"But I couldn't jump into the sea," said Tommy, "really I couldn't."

"Well, of course, Tommy," said the teacher, "nobody wants to jump into the sea. But if you have to, Tommy, I know you'll be a brave boy, won't you?"

Tommy was silent for a moment as he thought it over in his little head. Then, very solemnly he said, "Well, I'll promise not to mind if—if—if you'll promise to hold my hand!"

The teacher promised, and bidding Tommy good-by, went on his way.

I am glad to tell you that the promise did not have to be kept. The ship reached port in safety. Tommy did not have to jump overboard, and the teacher did not have to hold his hand. All three hundred children set foot at last upon the friendly shores of the New World.

But the memory of Tommy's courage and faith live on to bless us all today. For if that dear little boy of six was willing to jump into the cold, cruel sea if the teacher would hold his hand, then cannot we be brave when things go wrong with us? When something that we have to do looks cold and dark and dangerous, shall we not look up to the Great Teacher above and say to Him, "I'll promise not to mind if you'll promise to hold my hand."

And Jesus will hold it, never fear.

UNCLE ARTHUR'S
BEDTIME STORIES

Nineteenth Series

With Every Good Wish

To ....

From ....

V19A7

H. A. Roberts

Just a Little Bit of Love

Uncle Arthur's
BEDTIME STORIES
(NINETEENTH SERIES)

BY ARTHUR S. MAXWELL

"Even a child is known by his
doings, whether his work be
pure, and whether it be right."
Prov. 20:11.

REVIEW AND HERALD PUBLISHING ASSOCIATION

TAKOMA PARK, WASHINGTON, D. C.

PRINTED IN U. S. A.

CONTENTS

PREFACE

WAR or no war the children must have their "Bed-time Stories." So here comes the nineteenth series With twenty-three brand-new stories which I hope will bring much joy and inspiration to a great many children.

Purposely I have said little about all the trouble that is in the world today. It seemed to me that children see and hear enough about it anyway, and when bedtime comes, their "good night" story should leave them with happy memories, all ready for pleasant dreams.

So this year again I have followed the same pattern as I have these eighteen years since "Bedtime Stories" were first published. Each story is based on fact and each one is designed to convey some beautiful, character-building lesson. Many of them have been told to me personally by little children as I have traveled from place to place.

I should like to thank all those who have written to me in care of the publishers. Such letters are greatly appreciated; and to every one a personal reply is sent.

Those who are interested in the circulation of "Bedtime Stories" will be glad to know that, although it is impossible nowadays to gather the figures for certain foreign translations, the grand total is now approximately seven million copies.

That these new stories, like all those that have preceded them, may bring great blessing and happiness to children everywhere—not forgetting their parents, too, of course—is the sincere prayer of

THE AUTHOR.

5

Fortunate Is the Boy Who Has a Little Sister to Play With Him

Kenny's Comfort

IT was Kenny's bad luck, so he thought, to be the youngest in a family of five children. He had one big sister and three big brothers, and he—well, he was just the "little 'un."

Kenny didn't like being the "little 'un" for many reasons, but chiefly because his sister and his brothers were so big and so busy that they didn't have any time to play with him. During the day they would be away at school, and when they came home in the evening they would have homework to do; or they would want to go and play with friends of their own age.

So poor little Kenny felt quite lonely many times. How he did wish for a little sister—someone who would belong to him and play with him and be interested in the same things he was!

"Daddy," he would say sometimes, "can't you get me a baby sister somewhere? I do so want one."

And daddy would say, "I wish I could, dear; but they are very hard to find. I'll keep it in mind, though."

And then Kenny would say, "But, daddy, when you go traveling sometime, couldn't you just pick one up and bring her home with you? There must be lots of little girls who would like to come and live with me."

"It's not so easy as that," daddy would reply, "but I'll keep looking and maybe, one day—well, you never know what might happen."

So daddy went on his travels and told all his friends

7

about his lonely little boy at home who wanted a baby sister so very much that he was even praying for one. Oh, yes, I forgot to tell you that; Kenny was praying for a baby sister every night.

And some of daddy's friends smiled and thought it was very funny; but it wasn't funny to Kenny.

Then one day something happened.

Daddy opened a letter and it said: "Dear Sir: I have been told that you are looking for a baby girl. I happen to know of one who needs a home. She is just two-and-a-half years old and is a very sweet child. Perhaps you would like to come and see her."

Then daddy was scared and wished he hadn't told so many people about the poor lonely little boy who wanted a baby sister. He knew that he was, as people say, "on the spot," and had to decide one way or the other. He began to count up what it would cost to go and see the child, what it would cost to bring her home, what it would cost to feed her and clothe her for years and years and years.

Kenny wasn't worried, though. He thought it was just grand, and felt sure that his prayer was really going to be answered at last.

"Now don't get so excited," said daddy; "she may not be a bit nice—"

"But the letter says she is 'very sweet,'" said Kenny. "She must be nice."

"Well," said daddy, "maybe we won't think she is; and, anyway, perhaps something else will prevent our taking her. Just think what it will cost!"

"Oh, she won't cost much," said Kenny. "She's so little. And I'm sure she's nice. Of course she is. Anyway, daddy, you will go to see her?"

"Well, I don't know," said daddy. "It's a big risk. Er—er—just think—"

"Oh, don't think about it, daddy; just go," said Kenny.

So daddy went. There was really nothing else for him to do. And sure enough, at his journey's end, there she was, a tiny little thing with blue eyes and light curly hair—so thin and so wee and needing a home so very much.

What could he do? He looked her all over; he thought about Kenny; and then, completely forgetting all about the cost, he picked her up, and put her in his pocket—well, not quite, but almost—and brought her all the long, long way home.

When he reached home, there was Kenny, eagerly waiting on the doorstep, thrilled to the innermost parts of his lonely little soul.

No baby born could have had a warmer welcome. Kenny waited on her hand and foot, washing her face, her hands, her feet, when they got dirty—as they so often did—putting her to bed at night, dressing her in the morning, tying on her bib at mealtimes, and looking after her with almost a mother's care.

And how beautifully they played together! Kenny found his old tricycle and fixed it up so that Little Sister could ride on it. Of course, he was much too big for a tricycle now, and had a bicycle of his own. So round and round the house they would go, shrieking with delight and having the grandest time.

When they got tired of riding, Kenny would put Little Sister in his wagon and drag her hither and yon across the lawn and round the garden paths, running so fast that she had to hold on with all her might to keep from falling out.

They were so very happy that a stranger looking at them

might well have thought that they had known each other all their little lives.

Six months later daddy and Kenny were out alone together.

"Now, Kenny, don't you think it's about time we sent the little girl back?" said daddy.

"Oh, no!" cried Kenny.

"Do you really want to keep her?"

"Of course I do, always," said Kenny.

"But why?" asked daddy.

"'Cos she's my comfort," said Kenny.

And she really was. Never again did Kenny say he was lonely.

Locked in the Cupboard

WHILE we are still thinking about Kenny and his new little sister, I must tell you another story about them which could have been—but for her—one of the saddest stories ever told.

You see, they were playing hide-and-seek together, having such a happy time. First Kenny would hide, calling out "Ready!" when he was safely tucked away somewhere. Then Little Sister would wander all round the house and out in the garden, looking high and low for him. To tell you the truth, she wasn't very good at finding anything or anybody, perhaps because everything was so new to her; but she would hunt and hunt until at last she would come to the right place. Then there would be a big yell as both children saw each other again. After that, Little Sister would hide. At least, she would try to hide, for it was very difficult to go anywhere that Kenny did not know about; and soon there would be another big shout as she was discovered.

Now it so happened that a new cupboard had just been built in mother's laundry, which stood some distance away from the house, near the garage. As soon as the carpenter had finished it, Kenny said to himself, What a place to hide! He made up his mind that the very next chance he got, he would get inside that cupboard, and then Little Sister would never find him.

The chance soon came. Kenny crept silently into the laundry, and bending down low, managed to squeeze himself between the two bottom shelves of the cupboard. The

11

shelves, by the way, were about 26 inches wide and eleven inches deep, with sixteen inches between them!

Quite sure that he was well hidden this time, Kenny called, "Ready—y! Read—y!"

Suddenly a gust of wind swept through the open window of the laundry.   Click!

Hiding in the Cupboard

The latch of the door had snapped into place! Kenny was trapped inside, in pitch darkness, wedged between the two shelves!

Terrified, he called and called and called, but nobody heard him, for mother was out shopping, daddy was busy in the house, and Little Sister was looking everywhere else but in the laundry.

Meanwhile the tiny space inside the cupboard became hotter and hotter, for the only air that could come in entered by the crack at the edge of the door. Poor Kenny started to cry, as well he might. Then he prayed, oh, so hard, "Jesus, please send somebody to let me out."

Still nobody came.

He called and called.

There was no reply.

It got hotter and hotter, and more and more uncomfortable, for he was terribly cramped. He couldn't lift his head, or stretch his arms or legs. Even his toes were bent and he couldn't straighten them.

Ten minutes passed; twenty minutes; thirty minutes. And each minute seemed like a year.

Far away he could hear Little Sister calling, "Kenny, where are you?" But he couldn't tell her where he was, for the cupboard walls wouldn't let his voice travel so far.

Then he heard a sound that brought new hope to his poor little heart. It was the pat, pat, pat of tiny feet coming toward the laundry. Kenny had never heard such a welcome sound in all his life; it was like the footfalls of angels!

"Here I am!" he cried, and he heard the pat, pat, pat come right inside the laundry.

"Where are you?" asked Little Sister, looking round in wonder at hearing a voice but seeing nobody.

Standing on Tip-toe Little Sister Could Just Reach the Catch

14

"In the new cupboard," cried Kenny. "Come and open it quickly!"

"I can't," said Little Sister. "It's too high up."

"Oh, try, try," cried Kenny. "Stand on tiptoe and try."

Little Sister, frightened by the sound of Kenny's voice, tried her very best. She stood up on the very tips of her toes, and reached up just as high as she could. There was a click as she pressed back the catch, then a shout of joy as Kenny tumbled out from between the two shelves.

Can you guess what happened next? Well, Kenny picked Little Sister up in his arms and kissed her over and over again; and probably in all his life he will never forget how she came to his rescue and saved him from his terrible prison in the dark, hot cupboard.

Then they ran indoors to tell daddy all about it; and he said that he thought it was a very unwise thing for any little boy or girl to hide in a cupboard, for so many children who had done so had never been found until it was too late, and they had suffocated. He said that neither of them was to hide in a cupboard any more; and then he kissed them both and gave them each two pieces of candy.

And when they had gone out again, laughing and happy, he said to himself, What did I say about the cost of bringing home that darling wee thing? She has paid everything a million times over by what she did today!

H. M. Lambert

Tommy Blew and Blew and Blew!

16

Tommy's Trumpet

JUST why anybody should give a little boy a toy trumpet for a birthday present, I don't know. But people will do such things; and so Tommy found himself one day the proud owner of one of these noisy "musical" instruments.

Was he happy! He blew it and blew it and blew it, until he had everybody in the house in a very nervous state.

After a while there came a voice from daddy's study; and it didn't sound too appreciative of Tommy's efforts.

"Tommy, I can't stand that noise any longer! Please don't blow that trumpet any more."

"But it's my birthday, daddy."

"I know it's your birthday," said daddy, "and that's why I haven't said anything up to now; but there are limits."

"Well, could I blow it just a little while longer?"

"All right, just a little while, but not very long."

So Tommy blew it again, this time out in the garden. But forgetting his promise to blow only "a little while," he went on and on until a window went up with a bang and daddy's head was poked out.

"Tommy! Stop that noise!"

"Well, it's my birthday," said Tommy.

"I know it's your birthday," said daddy; "but that doesn't give you the right to annoy everybody for miles around."

"Well, could I blow it around the other side of the house? Nobody's in next door."

"All right then, but don't blow it so hard."

17

"All right, daddy."

But it didn't make much difference. The sound of that trumpet was so penetrating it seemed to go right through the house; although perhaps it echoed back from the other houses near by.

Presently the window went up again; this time with a bang as loud as the noise of Tommy's trumpet.

"Now that's enough!" cried daddy. "Quite enough for one day."

"But it's my birthday," said Tommy, coming slowly round the house.

"Maybe it is," said daddy firmly; "but that's all the more reason why you should be thoughtful of other people. Put that trumpet away!"

With much pouting and muttering, Tommy put it away. He couldn't understand why he shouldn't be allowed to blow it just as long as he wished. Why did daddy have to bother so?

Now it so happened that mother had prepared a delicious birthday supper for Tommy, with a big beautiful birthday cake. Because it was his birthday, Tommy thought he should be allowed to eat all he wanted; and he did.

Afterward during the night, he felt very sick; and when he woke up in the morning, he had a terrible headache. In fact, he felt so bad that when mother suggested that he should stay in bed, he did so without a grumble.

Just when he was feeling very bad, he heard a familiar sound downstairs. Little Sister was blowing his trumpet! And how loud she blew it! It was terrible, simply terrible! The noise fairly made his head split.

"Mamma! daddy!" he called. "Tell Sister to stop blowing my trumpet. I can't stand the noise."

Then he heard a voice from somewhere close by, and it sounded like daddy's. "I thought you liked trumpets," he said. "Remember yesterday morning?"

Tommy got the point right away. It's strange, but he was much more careful about blowing his trumpet after that.

When Tommy was better, daddy reminded him that it is always a good plan to "do unto others" as you would like to have them do to you.

H. M. Lambert

Who Made That Mess?

20

Who Made That Mess?

MOTHER was puzzled. Only an hour or two ago she had run the sweeper over the bedroom carpet, leaving it as clean as when it came from the store. Now, lo and behold, it was all covered with tiny white specks.

What could they be? They were so very small that she couldn't tell at first; but presently she found a bigger piece, and it seemed to be part of a paper handkerchief.

That's very strange, thought mother. Who could have torn up a paper handkerchief into such tiny little pieces and scattered them all over my nice clean floor?

She looked over at Helen, who was lying in her bed, fast asleep, taking her afternoon nap. The little girl looked so innocent that mother couldn't bring herself to believe that she had done it. Why, she had never done anything like this before, and how could she do it, anyway?

By and by Helen awoke and found mother in the bedroom.

"Hello, darling," said mother. "So you are awake at last. I've been waiting to ask you how all these little bits of paper got on the floor."

"I don't know," said Helen; "I wonder who could have put them there?" But the blush on her face told mother all she wanted to know.

"Well, I'm surprised you don't know anything about it," said mother, "but I'll clean up the mess and maybe we'll talk about it again later."

21

So mother brought out the sweeper and ran it over the carpet until it was quite clean again.   Then they went downstairs.

Mother didn't say another word about it that day.   She thought it might be best to wait and see what happened.

Next morning, before putting Helen to sleep, she made sure that there was not a speck of paper on the carpet.   Then she left a box of paper handkerchiefs close to Helen's cot.

When mother thought Helen was asleep, she went into the bedroom again, and believe it or not, there was the carpet all covered with tiny pieces of paper, just as it had been the day before.

Now what to do?   Should she wake Helen?   Mother decided not to do that; another idea came to her.

By and by Helen opened her eyes, and there was mother again, sitting close beside her.

"Well, darling," said mother, "I am glad you are awake. I want to ask you a question."

"Yes," said Helen, somewhat fearfully.

"Tell me about all those pieces of paper."

Helen was silent.

"Why did you do it?"

"I don't know."

"Well, do you know that you are a very naughty girl?"

"Yes."

"What do you think mother should do?"

"Don't know," said Helen, starting to cry.

"I am going to give you a choice," said mother.   "Shall mother spank, or will you pick up all the pieces?"

"I'll pick up all the pieces," said Helen very quickly.

And so she did.   Piece by piece the little fingers gathered them up.   How long it took I do not know, but it was a very long time. She gathered them up just as though she had been a little carpet sweeper herself, and when she had finished, the carpet was as clean as it had been before.

All that long, long time, Helen was thinking, and when finally she had picked up the last little piece, she had made up her mind that she would never tear up paper handkerchiefs again. What is more, she decided, too, that never again would she tell mother an untruth.

Somehow—how can it be?—mother always finds out.

Peter Pays Up

ⅩⅩ

PETER was staying with his grandma, and early one afternoon she suggested that they go shopping together. Peter was delighted. Very soon the two were on their way to town.

Arriving at a general store, they went inside and were met with a cheery "Good afternoon" from Mrs. Green, the smiling saleswoman behind the counter. Grandma went over to talk to her and buy the things she had written down on her list, while Peter wandered around looking at all the goods for sale.

What a lot of beautiful things there were! In one corner there was a pile of fresh brown loaves, and the most tempting cakes and pies. In another, under a glass case, there were bottles of milk, and packets of butter and cheese. Piled up on shelves there were all sorts of bright-colored cartons. In the center of the floor were baskets of fruit and vegetables. All together they made a very pleasant picture, and the mixture of delicious odors made Peter very, very hungry.

Maybe you know how it feels to take a long walk and then go into a store full of food. Well, Peter felt just like that, and since he was only five years old, perhaps you shouldn't blame him too much for what he did next.

It so happened that among the baskets of fruit there was one piled high with big, luscious blackberries. How Peter did love blackberries! He never could get enough of them and now, here in front of him, was a whole basketful of them!

24

He put out his hand to take one, but a little voice inside him seemed to say, "No, Peter; you mustn't do that; that would be stealing." But the berries looked so delicious that he felt he *had* to take one. After all, he thought, there were so many, many berries that nobody would ever notice if he just had one.

So Peter did not listen to his conscience. Instead he put out one of his chubby little hands and took just one blackberry. But that one tasted so good that he decided to take another one. How sweet it was!

Then, seeing that there seemed to be just as many left in the basket as there had been before, he took another one. And another. In fact, he was just getting settled to a real meal of blackberries when he heard a familiar voice from the other side of the shop.

"Peter! Peter! Where are you?" called grandma.

"Here I am, grandma," cried Peter, wiping his hands on the back of his trousers and hurrying round the pile of baskets.

"Come along, dear," said grandma. "We're all ready to go home now. Would you like to carry some of the packages? There's a dear boy. How good you have been all the time while grandma has been shopping!"

Peter blushed a little at this, as he took the packages grandma handed to him. Then they opened the door and went out.

Suddenly grandma stopped.

"Peter," she said, "look at me!"

Peter looked up, trying to appear as innocent as possible.

"What are those black marks on your face, Peter?" asked grandma.

"What black marks?" asked Peter.

Keystone

26   *Peter and Grandma Went Shopping at the General Store*

"All round your mouth, dear. Not quite black, but blackish red."

"I don't know," said Peter, although if he could have seen his dirty face, he would have owned up right away.

"Peter, you have been eating blackberries," said grandma. "Haven't you?"

Peter's head went down. "Just one or two," he said.

"Where did you get them?" asked grandma.

"In the store," said Peter.

"Did Mrs. Green say you could have them?"

"No."

"Do you mean you took them without asking?"

"Yes."

"Then Peter was a very naughty boy," said grandma, "and I am very much ashamed of him. Come along, let's go home and we will see what should be done about it."

Peter began to cry, and it was a very sad walk they had together, so different from the journey they had taken but a little while before.

When they got indoors grandma took Peter on her knee and told him how very wrong it is to take things that belong to other people; that it is breaking the commandment which says, "Thou shalt not steal." She also told him that there were just two things he had to do. One was to ask God to forgive him, and the other was to go to Mrs. Green, pay her for the berries he had eaten, and tell her how sorry he was that he had taken them.

"I don't mind asking God to forgive me," said Peter, crying; "but I don't want to ask Mrs. Green."

"I know it's hard," said grandma; "but it's the only way. Now go and find your purse."

"You mean I have to pay for the berries myself?"

"Surely you must," said grandma.

"But it will take all my money," said Peter.

"Never mind if it takes all you have," said grandma. "You must make it right. But I don't think it will take all. In fact, I think a nickel would pay for all that you ate."

"A whole nickel!" said Peter. "Do I have to give Mrs. Green a whole nickel?"

"Yes," said grandma. "And the sooner you go down to see her the better. Wipe your eyes now and be a big, brave man."

Peter wiped them with the backs of his hands, and grandma kissed him good-by. Holding his nickel tightly, he set off for the store.

How far away it seemed, as he dragged one weary foot after the other! But at last the store came in sight and, with his heart beating hard, he went inside.

"What! Back again so soon!" exclaimed Mrs. Green. "Did grandma forget something?"

"No," said Peter slowly, "I did."

"You did!" said Mrs. Green. "What did you forget?"

"Mrs. Green, er—er—I—er—er—please, I forgot to pay for the blackberries I ate. And—er—er—please, grandma said they're worth a nickel. So I've brought it out of my very own purse and—er—er—please, I'm very sorry I didn't ask you about them first."

And with that Peter put the nickel on the counter, turned around, and ran for the door. Opening it, he dashed outside, and started to run home. But he had not gone far when he heard Mrs. Green calling him.

"Peter!" she said. "I want you a minute. Come back here."

Very slowly Peter went back, as though expecting to be scolded.

"You forgot something else," said Mrs. Green, smiling, and handing him a paper bag.

"No," said Peter, "I didn't leave that."

"But it's for you, anyway," said Mrs. Green. "Just something good for your supper." Then she patted him on the head and told him to run home quickly. Peter thought he saw tears in her eyes, but he wasn't quite sure, and he couldn't think why.

How he did run then! It seemed as though he was home almost before he had started.

"Look what she gave me!" he cried. "Grandma, look!"

Grandma looked. It was a delicious-looking big doughnut, with jam inside.

"Aren't you glad you went back and made things right?" said grandma.

"Am I!" exclaimed Peter.

"It's always the best thing to do," said grandma.

It surely is.

H. M. Lambert

Joan Looking at the Water Lilies

30

That Pond Again!

IN Johnnie's garden there was a beautiful pond, complete with water lilies, goldfish, and a bridge. Oh, yes, and a waterfall, too; that is, when daddy turned on the water, which he did when visitors came to see it.

Winding in and out amid little dwarf trees and bushes, the pond made this part of the garden very pretty indeed; and it was so innocent looking that a stranger would never suspect that boys and girls could get into trouble there.

Not that anybody could drown in it. Oh, dear, no; for it was only a foot deep or thereabouts; but there are other things that can happen to people in ponds besides getting drowned.

So many things had, in fact, happened at this particular pond that mother had laid down the law that the children were not to play anywhere near it without her special permission.

"No," she had said this very morning; "it's no use coaxing, Johnnie. You cannot play at the pond today. Your clothes are hardly dry from the last time you fell in. What's more, you know Mrs. Norman is coming today with Mary."

"Is Mary coming today?"

"She is."

"Goody!" cried Johnnie. "Now we shall have some fun."

"But not at the pond," said mother, "because you will have your best clothes on. So you and Joan keep away from it. See?"

"All right, mamma," said Johnnie, while little Joan echoed, "Awite."

But everything was not "all right," even though Johnnie and Joan said it was. For Mary was a very lively little girl, and as soon as she arrived she cried out in great joy, "Oh, what a lovely pond! Johnnie, let's go and play at the pond!"

Johnnie's sailboat was riding at anchor in one of the little bays, and Mary rushed across the garden toward it. Johnnie followed, with Joan behind him, both of them dressed in their best for Mrs. Norman's benefit.

By the time they reached the pond, Mary was down on her knees, reaching out toward the boat. She wanted to give it a push and send it across the water.

"What a beautiful boat!" she cried. "We must have a game with it."

"I'll get it for you," said Johnnie, picking up a stick— quite forgetting what mother had said such a little while ago.

"Don't bother," said Mary. "I can reach it. You'll see."

Johnnie did see—much more than he expected—for Mary, straining to reach the boat, lost her balance and fell flat into the dirty, greenish-looking water!

Splash!

Right under the water she went, with her smart new shoes, her pretty new dress, and her golden-brown curls. Of course, she didn't stay there very long; just long enough to get herself into a dreadful mess. Then Johnnie, reaching over to lift her out, fell in himself!

What a sight the two made as they walked back to the house, with water running off their hair, dripping from their clothes, and oozing out of their shoes!

If you could have seen mother's face as she saw them

coming! That was a sight, too! It said a great many things all at once.

Then came the undressing, or rather the unpeeling, for they were both so wet that their clothes stuck to them like the peel to an orange. When their clothes were off, they had to be washed and dried, while mother hurried round looking for something else for them to wear. Just as they were in the middle of all this, from far down the garden came the sound of someone screaming.

"Oh, dear, that's Joan!" cried mother. "Something must have happened to her."

It had.

As they all rushed out of the house to find out what was the matter now, they saw a tiny little form trying its best to scramble out on the bank of the pond! It was Joan. At least, it was all that was left of her and her pretty new dress. She had been trying to pick a water lily and had met the same sad fate as Mary.

Just what mother's face looked like at this moment nobody could describe. It said even more than it had before.

And when Mrs. Norman and Mary had gone home— Mary in some of Johnnie's old clothes—mother turned her thoughts into words, and actions.

"When I say keep away from the pond," she said, as she rested her right hand, "I mean keep away from the pond— no matter who comes to see you, or whatever he may say to you."

For some reason that you may guess Johnnie and Joan never disobeyed mother on this point again.

34

Don't Play With Kettles—or Gas Stoves

Why Mother Says Don't!

∞

JOE, don't touch that kettle!" cried mother. "It's nearly boiling."

"I was only lifting it to see how much water was inside," said Joe rather crossly. "I wasn't going to hurt anything."

"But it isn't safe for you to touch a boiling kettle; you might do some damage."

"Oh, all right," said Joe; but he continued to stand by the stove. It wasn't long before his busy fingers were turning on the gas jets.

"Joe!" cried mother, as she turned around from her work and saw what he was up to now. "Joe! Leave that stove alone and don't ever let me see you playing with the gas again."

"All right," said Joe, and he wandered off to look for something else to do.

He picked up a piece of wood from beside the fireplace and began whittling at it with the carving knife, which was lying temptingly on the kitchen table.

He had not got very far when mother called again.

"Joe! What are you doing now? Put that knife down. It's terribly sharp. Don't ever use it for whittling."

"All right," said Joe, putting the knife back on the table. "All right. I'll do something else."

This time he sat down on the floor and started going through his pockets. In one of them he found a piece of wire. For a while he amused himself by bending it into vari-

35

ous shapes.   Then he started to poke it into the electric wall plug.

Suddenly there was a bang in the fuse box up on the kitchen wall and all the lights went out.

"Joe!" exclaimed mother. "What have you done now?"

"Nothing," said Joe. "I was just poking this little piece of wire into this hole in the wall!"

"Joe, you bad boy!   Haven't I told you before that you must never play with electricity?   Now you've blown the fuse and put all the lights out. Don't you ever do that again."

"All right," said Joe, mumbling to himself, as he walked off into the dining room.

Mother got a stepladder and climbed up to fix the fuse. As she worked away at it, she could hear Joe saying to himself, "It's just don't, don't, don't, and then don't, don't, don't."   So mother thought it was about time that she explained.

When it came time for Joe to go to bed and mother went upstairs to tuck him in and kiss him good night—Joe still loved to have her do that—she said, "Do you wonder, sometimes, Joe, why mamma has to say, 'Don't, don't, don't'?"

"Yes," said Joe, as a curious look came into his eyes. How did mother know what he had been thinking?

"Well, it's this way, darling.   When I say 'Don't,' it's always for your good.   Remember about the kettle this afternoon?   Why did I say, 'Don't touch it'?   Because if you had tried to lift it off the stove, you would very likely have spilled the boiling water over yourself or over Little Brother; and then what trouble we should have had!   And you would have been more sorry than anybody else, wouldn't you?"

"Of course I would," said Joe.

"Then about the stove. If you turn on those gas jets just when you want to do so, the gas may do all sorts of damage. You may burn something that I am cooking, or make something boil over, or—worse still—set the house on fire. You wouldn't want that to happen?"

"Oh, no," said Joe.

"Well, then," said mother, "that's why I have to say, 'Don't touch the stove.' And there's another reason. If you touch it, then Little Brother will think he can touch it, too, and who knows what trouble that might mean?"

Keystone

Don't Whittle With a Carving Knife

"I see," said Joe.   "But why did you tell me not to touch the knife?   I was only whittling a piece of firewood."

"I know, dear," said mother, "but one little slip with that sharp knife and your hand could have been badly cut. It could cut a finger to the bone before you could think about it.   When you whittle, use your own penknife—not a big dangerous knife like that."

"Well, but I didn't cut myself with it," said Joe.

"I know you didn't," said mother, "and I am very thankful; but you might have.   And now about the electricity.   I hardly need to tell you why you mustn't play with that."

"Because I blew the fuse," said Joe.

"Yes, but that's not all," said mother.   "While electricity is very useful in the right place, in the wrong place it may be very dangerous."

"What do you mean?"

"Just this, dear.   If, when you were playing with that wire, you had been standing in a pool of water; or if you had had one hand on the gas pipe, or on some other metal connected with the ground, the electricity might have jumped right through you, and then you would have been badly burned, or possibly killed."

"Ooo, might I?" asked Joe.

"Yes," said mother, "and I hope you see now that when I say, 'Don't,' there is a good reason why.   I say it, not because I don't love you, but because I do."

At this mother kissed Joe good night, and he turned over and went to sleep.   Next day, when mother said, "Don't," about something, he obeyed at once and gave her a happy little smile as if to say he understood.

Dennis and the Dive Bombers

xxxxxxxxxxxxxxxxxxxxxxxxxxxxxxxxxxxxxxxxxxxxxxxxxxxxxxxxxxxxxxxxxxxxxxxxx

IT looked as though all the little boys in the neighborhood were going off to war. Little Dennis stood at the gate of his home and watched with wide-open, eager eyes as they hurried by.

Some of them carried wooden guns over their shoulders; some had wooden swords; and others had pointed sticks that were supposed to be spears.

"Where are you going?" he called to some of the boys he knew.

"Come on!" they cried excitedly. "We're going to fight the enemy."

"Who's the enemy?" asked Dennis.

"We've found a wasps' nest out in the woods and we're all going out to do battle with them."

Dennis ran indoors.

"Mamma!" he cried. "May I go to war with all the other boys?"

"Whatever's this nonsense?" asked mother.

"They're all going out to the woods to fight the wasps, and they all have swords and guns and things. Let me go too—please, mamma."

Just then daddy came on the scene and asked, just as mother had, "What's all this nonsense?" And when he heard about it, he said that Dennis was not to go under any circumstances.

"It's a very foolish errand," he said. "Wasps can be very dangerous enemies, and one must be properly prepared

39

to fight them. You can't hope to succeed with pieces of wood. No, Dennis. You can't go."

So that was that, and Dennis had to content himself with standing at the gate waiting for the boys to come back.

After what seemed an age, the boys came rushing past, waving their weapons in the air and shouting about their great victory, although just what they had done to the wasps he never did find out.

Two days later he saw the boys going by the house again, just as they had done before, each one with his "weapon" of war.

"Come on, Dennis," they cried. "Don't be a sissy!"

"Father says I mustn't come," he said.

"Oh, come on," they called; "he won't mind. It's going to be great fun."

Dennis wavered. He could go with the boys and get back without daddy's knowing anything about it, for he was away at his office and wouldn't be back for hours. It would be such fun to go with the others, and he did so want to find out just how they fought wasps with wooden swords and spears.

So picking up a piece of wood to make a weapon for himself, he sallied forth to the battle.

On reaching the woods, some of the bigger boys began searching about for a wasps' nest, and it was not long before one of them called, "I have one. Here it is. And my, aren't they big fellows!"

They *were* big fellows. Unfortunately, they were not wasps at all, but hornets, and before long *they* were going into battle, while the poor boys were running pell-mell in every direction.

One of the hornets lit on poor Dennis, stinging him on his

upper lip, just under his nose. In a few moments there was a huge swelling that was, oh, so painful!

How he wished as he hurried homeward that he had not disobeyed his daddy! What would he say? And could anything daddy would do be more terrible than the awful pain he was suffering?

When mother saw what had happened, she was so frightened that she called the doctor. Then followed treatment after treatment until Dennis almost wished he would die. In fact, he suffered so much that daddy felt he had had more than sufficient punishment. But one day, when Dennis was almost better, daddy said, "Well, Dennis, so the boys didn't win that battle they went out to fight."

"No," said Dennis. "The enemy had too many dive bombers. We couldn't do a thing."

"I can think of another reason," said daddy. "Two of them, in fact."

"What?" asked Dennis.

"First, you didn't have proper equipment—no A. A. guns; and second, you acted without orders."

"Maybe you're right, daddy," said Dennis.

"I know I am," said daddy.

And, of course, he was.

H. A. Roberts

"Good Night, Margaret," Said Mamma

Sleeping With the Birdies

IT was Margaret's bedtime, and mother was taking her upstairs to put her in her nice comfy cot. All of a sudden the little girl burst into tears.

"What is the matter?" asked mother. "Have you hurt yourself?"

"No," said Margaret between her sobs.

"Well, then, what has happened?"

"Nuffin."

"Then why are you crying?"

"'Cos, 'cos, I don't want to sleep here."

"What do you mean?" asked mother. "Don't you want to sleep in this pretty bedroom and in your own little cot?"

"No."

"Well, then, where do you want to sleep?"

Margaret sobbed some more.

"Aren't you going to tell me?"

"Yes."

"Well, then, where *do* you want to sleep?"

"I want to sleep wiv the birdies."

"With the birdies!" exclaimed mother. "Why with the birdies?"

"I wan to sleep wiv the birdies," repeated Margaret.

"You mean outside in the garden?" asked mother.

"Yes."

"But it will soon be all dark out there. You wouldn't like that."

"I want to sleep wiv the birdies," said Margaret again.

43

"All right," said mother. "If you want so very much to sleep with the birdies, you shall. Let's go downstairs again."

So mother and Margaret went slowly downstairs into the hall. Then mother opened the front door, and the two went outside and stood for a moment on the steps.

"Good night, Margaret," said mother, giving her a big kiss. "I hope you have a quiet sleep with the birdies."

"Good night, mamma," said Margaret, and away she went.

Mother shut the door and wondered what would happen next.

She did not have very long to wait.

From somewhere out in the garden she heard a little girl crying piteously. Soon a little hand was banging on the front door.

"Well, darling," said mother, "you're back soon. Weren't the birdies good to you?"

"It's all dark and cold outside," wailed Margaret.

"I told you it was," said mother, "but you said you wanted to sleep with the birdies."

"I don't want to sleep wiv the birdies any more," wailed Margaret.

"Well, then, where do you want to sleep this time?"

"In my own little cot upstairs."

So upstairs they went again; and as soon as they were in the bedroom, Margaret was as happy as could be. She got into her cot and, snuggling down, went right off to sleep without another word.

Never once since then has she grumbled about going to bed when mother says it is bedtime.

Trickles of Kindness

BERTIE and Bobbie were supposed to be helping daddy tidy up the garden, but they were not making much progress.

"It's my turn to mow the lawn," said Bertie. "You can weed the flower bed."

"I don't want to weed the flower bed," said Bobbie. "I want to mow the lawn. It's my turn to mow, anyway. You give me that lawn mower."

"You shan't have it!" said Bertie. "Go and do your weeding."

"I won't!" cried Bobbie. "Give me the lawn mower."

"Shan't!" cried Bertie, running off at high speed, pushing the mower in front of him, with Bobbie at his heels. Of course, the mower was upside down; it wasn't cutting the lawn. No, indeed!

Round and round they went, both of them getting hotter and angrier all the time.

"Go—and—do—your—weeding!" panted Bertie.

"Give—me—that—lawn—mower!" panted Bobbie.

"Shan't—you—nasty—boy!" said Bertie.

"Yes—you—will—you horrid thing!" cried Bobbie.

Just as they were coming to blows, there was a loud grinding, banging noise from somewhere round the back of the house.

The two boys stood still and listened.

"It's the pump!" they cried together, running to see what had happened. As they ran they heard a loud report from

45

the top of the big pole supporting the electric wires and the main fuse.

"Here's a nice kettle of fish," said daddy, who was already on the scene. "The pump's gone wrong again; and that means no water until we can get it fixed."

"No water!" exclaimed Bertie. "You mean I can't have a drink?"

"No," said daddy. "And you can't have a bath—you can't even wash your face."

"What will mother do?" asked Bobbie. "She won't be able to wash the dishes or cook the dinner."

"No," said daddy. "It's going to be very inconvenient for all of us until the pump man comes. And all because of such a little thing."

"What little thing?" asked Bertie.

"Just this," said daddy. "You see, boys, this pump is water lubricated."

"What's that?" asked Bobbie.

"Well, in order that the pump won't get hot and stick to the sides of the well, a little trickle of water flows back from the tank all the time. Even when the pump isn't working, the trickle still flows on. In this way all the parts are kept moist and free, ready for when the motor begins to turn."

"But suppose the trickle of water stops?" said Bertie. "What happens then?"

"Just what you see now," said daddy. "I don't know what caused it to stop this time—the pump man will have to find that out—but this is the effect of it—a great deal of trouble and expense."

"It's too bad," said Bobbie, trying to be sympathetic.

"It is," said daddy. "And do you know, boys, it reminds me of what happened on the lawn this afternoon."

Bertie and Bobbie blushed very red, for they suddenly remembered their quarrel over the lawn mower; they had not thought that their angry words had been overheard.

Silent now, they wondered what daddy would say next.

"It's like this," he said. "As long as we let a trickle of kindness run through our hearts, everything goes along smoothly and happily. We think kind thoughts about other people and try to do kind, helpful things for them. We do not always demand our own way. We find happiness in making other people happy. But if the trickle of kindness dries up—well, what a lot of trouble and bother we do have! It's just like the grinding and the banging and the popping when the pump goes wrong."

Bertie and Bobbie couldn't help smiling. It was all *so* true! They began to think how they had chased each other round the lawn, making such a terrible fuss, even calling each other ugly names.

"You can have the lawn mower, Bobbie," said Bertie.

"No; you can have it," said Bobbie. "I'll do the weeding this time."

So the little trickles of kindness began to flow again

Kidnaped!

HAVE you ever wondered what it would be like to be kidnaped? Perhaps you have asked yourself just what you would do if a stranger suddenly picked you up and hurried you away in his car. Well, here is the story of a little boy who had this experience. I know it is true, for his mother wrote and told me all about it.

I am going to call him Raymond, for, of course, he wouldn't want me to use his real name.

He was just six years old at the time this happened, but though he was very young, he loved to do what he called his "missionary work." That is, when the minister at his church said that he needed money to send to the missionaries in foreign lands, Raymond would set out bravely to call at the neighbors' homes and tell them all about it. It was really surprising how much money he would bring home sometimes.

One day, in the summer of 1942, Raymond had been out collecting his "missionary money." He was almost finished. As he was walking home along a country road, he suddenly heard a car slow down and stop beside him. A strange man put his head out of the window and asked Raymond whether he wanted a ride.

"No, thank you," said Raymond, remembering his mother's strict warning that he was never to accept a ride from a stranger.

"Oh, come on," said the man.

"Thank you; I'd rather walk," said Raymond. "I do not have very far to go."

The stranger opened the door and got out.

"Get in there," he ordered, picking Raymond up bodily and shoving him on the front seat.

"But I don't want to ride!" shouted Raymond. "Let me out!"

It was no use. Already the door was shut and the man was starting the car. Soon they were moving rapidly along the road.

"What's your name?" asked the stranger.

"Raymond."

"Who's your father?"

Raymond told him.

"How much money does he earn?"

"Don't know," said Raymond. And at the mention of money he became more frightened, for he remembered the "missionary money" in his pocket which he had gathered that very afternoon. He hoped this bad man would not find out about it.

Now the car was speeding past his home, and Raymond saw all the old familiar places being left behind.

Oh, dear! he thought, where is he going to take me?

Then he remembered that mother had said that if he was working for Jesus, he need never be afraid, for the angels would surely look after him. So he began to say a little prayer; but he was so frightened that he said it out loud.

"What was that you were saying?" asked the man.

"I was asking Jesus to save me," said Raymond, as the tears rolled down his cheeks.

"Oh, very well, then, very well," said the man, putting his foot on the brake. "Get out, get out!"

With that he stopped the car, opened the door, and pushed Raymond onto the grass at the side of the road.

Then he jumped in again, and the car roared away into the distance.

As Raymond stood there wondering what to do next, a woman from a near-by farm came up to him and asked, "What in the world are you doing all alone out here?"

Raymond told her all that had happened. Getting her own car, she soon hurried him back to his mother.

Mother said he was a very brave boy, but Raymond said he was quite sure all the time that Jesus would help him because of the "missionary money" he had in his pocket that afternoon.

I think He did, too, don't you?

Freddie's Failing

xxxxxxxxxxxxxxxxxxxxxxxxxxxxxxxxxxxxxxxxxxxxxxxxxxxxxxxxxxxxxxxxx

LITTLE Freddie was like some other boys and girls I know. If his mother wanted him to do something for her, he would always say that he would rather do something else.

For instance, if mother said, "Now, Freddie, please come and dry the dishes for me," as likely as not Freddie would say, "Oh, I'd rather clear the table."

If mother said, "Freddie, please run next door and borrow half a pound of butter from Mrs. Jones," Freddie would probably say, "I don't want to go all that way; couldn't I put some coal on the fire?"

It was always "something else;" never just exactly what mother wanted. And that can be very troublesome sometimes.

One day—a very busy day—mother said, "Freddie, please set the table for supper. I've been hard at work all day and am very tired. There's a good boy."

"But I don't want to set the table," said Freddie; "couldn't I go and feed the chickens instead?"

"But I want you to set the table," said mother; "the chickens can wait a while."

"I know," said Freddie; "but I want to feed the chickens."

"Oh, very well," said mother, too weary after washing and ironing all day to bother with his contrariness. "Go and feed the chickens then."

Freddie went out the back door and walked slowly down

the garden to the chickens, taking time to kick a ball about on the way, as well as to talk to the little boy next door. Indeed, he took so much time to feed the chickens that it was quite late when he returned.

Opening the kitchen door, he was surprised to notice that the table was still bare.

"Aren't we going to have any supper tonight?" he called.

There was no reply.

"Mamma! Mamma!" he cried.

Silence.

He ran upstairs, still calling.

"Mamma! Mamma!"

No answer.

Now he began to be anxious. Where could mother have gone? Why didn't she have his supper ready? Didn't she know he was hungry?

"Mamma! Mamma!"

He went to the back door and shouted again.

This time there came a voice from next door.

"Oh, is that you, Freddie?"

"Aren't you coming?" cried Freddie. "Nobody's set the table."

"Oh, I want to talk to Mrs. Jones," said mother. "Don't worry. I'll be back soon."

And with that mother went back into Mrs. Jones's house and shut the door.

Poor Freddie, who was feeling very hungry by now, sat down on a kitchen chair.

"I wonder why mother didn't get my supper ready?" he asked himself. "She has never forgotten about it before."

Then he remembered that mother had asked *him* to set the table, and he had gone off to feed the chickens instead.

"Maybe, maybe—" he said to himself, "maybe mother isn't going to get my supper ready."

Some tears began to trickle down his cheeks, for it was very quiet and lonely sitting there by himself in the gathering darkness.

Then suddenly the door opened and in came mother. Freddie thought he had never been so glad to see her before.

"May I set the table now?" he asked before mother could say a word. "I'll be ever so quick, really I will, mamma."

"All right, Freddie," said mother. "I was going to let you go to bed without any supper, but I think you have learned your lesson."

"Yes, I am sure I have," said Freddie eagerly, as he ran to get the dishes out of the cupboard.

"I hope so," said mother. "In the future you had better remember to do just what mother says, right away."

"I will," said Freddie. "Sure, I will!"

May he never forget his promise!

There It Was on the Floor!

How Terence Got His Train

xxxxxxxxxxxxxxxxxxxxxxxxxxxxxxxxxxxxxxxxxxxxxxxxxxxxxxxxxxxxxxxxxxxxxxxxxxxx

FOR a very long time—it seemed to him like years and years—Terence had wanted an electric train. Whenever he saw one in a toyshop, he would stare at it just as long as his mother would let him stand at the window. He thought that if only he could have an electric train, all his very own, he would be the happiest boy in the world.

Over and over again he had come to daddy and said, "Please, daddy, do get me an electric train for my birthday;" or, "Please, daddy, do get me an electric train for Christmas;" but every time daddy had replied, "Sorry, Terence, but they are far too expensive, and what is more, it is almost impossible to buy an electric train nowadays."

Then Terence would go on hoping and hoping that someday, maybe, he would be able to buy one himself. The only trouble about that, however, was that Terence never seemed to have any money. If anybody gave him a penny or a dime, he would spend it right away for some candy, or some little thing he had seen in the toyshop, and so, of course, he had nothing saved up for anything so expensive as an electric train.

One day he came running home from school greatly excited.

"Daddy!" he cried. "Daddy! There's a boy at school who has an electric train, and he wants to sell it. May I buy it?"

"Surely you may, dear," said daddy, "if you have enough money." You see, daddy knew all about Terence's weakness where money was concerned. In fact, he often said that Terence had "a hole in his pocket."

"I don't have any money," said Terence, crestfallen. "At least, I don't have any except that dime you gave me the other day. I haven't spent that yet."

"How much does the boy want for his train?" asked daddy.

"Only twenty dollars," said Terence, "and he says that is very cheap because it includes all the carriages and rails and things."

"Twenty dollars!" exclaimed daddy. "It may be cheap, but that's a lot of money these days. I'm afraid your one little dime won't go very far."

"I'm afraid it won't," said Terence.

"Do you know how many dimes there are in twenty dollars?" asked daddy.

"No," said Terence, "I never added them up."

"Well, there are two hundred," said daddy.

"Phew!" whistled Terence; "that's a lot of dimes. But I thought maybe *you* might want to buy the train, daddy—"

"No, thanks," said daddy. "I really don't need an electric train just now. Thanks all the same."

Terence thought he would try another approach.

"If I were to save up two hundred dimes—" he began.

"Ha, ha!" laughed daddy. "You save two hundred dimes! Why, you have never saved half a dozen."

"But, daddy, I never wanted an electric train before."

"Well, you have been talking about an electric train for a mighty long time," said daddy; "and you have saved only one dime; that doesn't look as if you wanted it very much."

Terence blushed a little at this, but he was determined now. He really was.

"Look here, daddy," he said. "I'm going to save my money from now on. And when I have two hundred dimes, I'll buy that train."

"I'm afraid it'll be rusty by the time you get it," said daddy, smiling. "But I'll tell you what I'll do. When you have saved ten dimes—if you ever do—I'll give you ten more toward your train; and so on until you have enough."

"Will you, daddy?" cried Terence, jumping about in glee. "Now I can get my train."

"I wouldn't be too sure about it," smiled daddy, feeling that his contribution was pretty safe. "After all, you do have quite a long way to go. By the way, how do you propose to earn so much money?"

"I'm going over right now to ask Mrs. Brown whether I may mow her lawn every week. Then I shall ask Mr. Morgan if I may sweep up the leaves in his garden. Then I shall—"

"Now you're talking sense," said daddy. "That's fine. Maybe I could find you a few jobs, too, if you want them."

"Surely I do," said Terence. "Oh, daddy, I can almost hear that train running round my bedroom now!"

So Terence started on his great new plan. Instead of wasting his spare minutes, he turned them into money, dime by dime. It was hard, of course; but then, every good thing costs something. When his friends would come to ask him to play ball or go swimming, he would say, "Sorry, but I have a job to do." It was hard—dreadfully hard—to see them go off without him, but just as he felt tempted to throw up his work and follow them, he would think of his electric train and stay by his job.

Yes, and he stopped spending his money on trifles, too, such as cheap toys that get broken in a few minutes. Instead he would take his precious dimes and put them in his bank. Of course, every time he had ten extra ones in it, he would call on daddy for his ten.

Daddy began to get anxious. He seemed to be paying out ten dimes every week or two. But somehow he didn't mind too much, for he could see that Terence was learning lessons of priceless value.

Months passed by and the precious bank became heavier and heavier. Then one day—the very day before Terence's birthday—something tragic happened.

Terence came home from school brokenhearted. There were tears in his eyes, and some on his cheeks, too.

"What's the matter?" asked daddy.

"That boy's sold his train," said Terence, breaking down. "And now I can't have one after all."

"That's too bad," said daddy. "Too bad. But I'll tell you, Terence, I was afraid of it all the time. You could hardly expect him to wait so long."

"I know, but I thought he would," said Terence.

"Well," said daddy, "now you will be able to save the money for something else."

"I don't want anything else but my train," said Terence. "It's a shame. He's a mean, nasty boy for selling it."

"Don't take it so hard," said daddy. "Let's go for a walk together and try to forget all about it."

"A walk!" exclaimed Terence. "I don't want to go for a walk. And I'll never forget about it so long as I live!"

"Oh, just a little walk upstairs," said daddy.

"Upstairs?" asked Terence, curious at once. "Why upstairs?"

"Oh, just a little walk," said daddy.

Very much puzzled, Terence followed daddy upstairs.

As he entered his bedroom, his tear-stained face suddenly lighted up with surprise and joy. There it was on the floor— the very electric train he had wanted so long and worked so hard to buy.

"Why, it's my train!" he exclaimed. "How did it get here?"

"Oh, it just came," said daddy.

"Go on!" said Terence. "It couldn't just have come by itself."

"I know," said daddy. "I bought it from that boy weeks ago. When I saw the way you were working for it, I thought it would be too bad to have him get tired of waiting for your money and sell it to somebody else. So here it is. And you deserve it. I love to see a boy work hard and save hard, as you have done."

"Hurrah!" yelled Terence, jumping right over his bed. "Oh, say, daddy, if you'd like to come and play with this train any time, you can, you know."

"Thanks!" said daddy. And the two sat down on the floor together and turned on the switch.

Ungrateful Gertie

THIS story is about a very kind lady and a very naughty little girl.

I used to know the kind lady quite well, and she told me all about it; so, of course, I know it is true.

Not far from where I live there is a grocery store which sells candy—and a great many other things besides, of course. One day the kind lady was buying some goods in this store when the door opened and in rushed five children, one boy and four little girls.

The children pressed close to the counter and began to look over all the candy that was for sale. After much talking about what they liked best, they finally put their pennies down and took the candy they wanted. That is, all except one little girl, who did not have a penny. Perhaps she had lost hers. I don't know, but when all the others ran out of the store sucking their lollipops or munching their chocolate bars, she trailed behind, looking very sorry for herself.

In fact, this poor little girl looked so sad that she made the kind lady feel sad, too, and in less time than it takes to tell, she had left her parcels on the counter and started to follow the children down the street.

There they were, not very far away. The boy in front, three girls behind him, and the little one just behind them. The kind lady thought she had never seen anything so mean and unkind, for the four in front were still busily eating their sweets while the little one had none.

So the kind lady hurried along, caught up with the little

girl, and asked her if she would not like to come back to the store with her and get some candy for herself.

The little girl said she would, and the two walked back down the street together.

"What's your name, dear?" asked the kind lady tenderly.

"Gertie," said the little girl.

"That's a nice name," said the kind lady. "Do you like candy?"

"Yes," said Gertie.

Going back into the store, the kind lady asked Gertie which candy she would like, and the little girl pointed to several things, all of which the kind lady bought for her.

Then what do you suppose happened? It was dreadful. I can hardly believe it, but it's true. That naughty little girl grabbed the bag of candy and, without even looking at the kind lady, dashed out of the door and down the street.

Did she say, "Thank you"? She did not.

Did she give the lady a sweet smile of gratitude? She did not.

A few minutes later I happened to meet the kind lady. She was not feeling very well pleased about it, I can tell you. Would you like to know what she said?

"The ungrateful little wretch!" she exclaimed. Though she smiled when she said it, I knew she felt very sad right inside her kind old heart. "I'll never do it again," she added. "Never."

And, if the truth must be told, she never did. For only a little while after that the kind lady passed away. How sad that almost her last thought was of ungrateful Gertie, the little girl who forgot to say, "Thank you."

H. A. Roberts

Even Big Engines Like This Need a "Helper Engine" Now and Then

The Helper Engine

NOT long ago I was riding in one of the fine express trains that run from San Francisco to Los Angeles in California. The scenery had been quite flat and uninteresting for some time, so that as I sat in my comfortable seat I was gradually becoming more and more sleepy. However, just before I went right off to sleep I heard a voice speaking over the public address system which is installed on these special trains.

"We are approaching the mountains," said the voice. "The train will soon be climbing at the rate of 110 feet every mile. Because one engine is not able to pull the train up so steep a climb, we shall be stopping in a few minutes to take on a helper engine."

By that time, of course, I was quite wide-awake. A helper engine! That sounded so interesting that I wanted to see one.

Very soon the train began to slow down to a stop. There was a gentle bump as the helper engine was hooked on, and then we started up the mountains.

How easily the train climbed up and up and up! No fuss or bother. In fact, if I hadn't been able to see the mountains from the train window I wouldn't have known we were climbing at all.

As the track wound this way and that, sometimes almost making a complete circle, up the steep grade, I sometimes got a brief glimpse of the helper engine. There it was, coupled to the main engine, puffing away in unison with it. That is when the main engine gave a puff, the helper engine gave a puff, and so they went on and up together.

Soon we were over the mountains, and the helper engine was uncoupled. Back it went to help another train up the steep slope.

Then I began to think of all the little engines in people's homes which could be such a help if they would.

"Engines?" you say. "We don't have any engines in our home."

Oh, yes, you do! Big ones and little ones, too. One of the big engines, of course, is daddy, and what a load he has to pull as he toils to earn the money to keep the home to-gether! How hard it must be sometimes to drag the long train of all the family needs—and wants—up the steep mountains of life!

Another engine is called "Mamma," and how she does have to work to keep the place tidy and do the washing and prepare all the meals and look after the sick folks! What a climb it is for her sometimes!

Then there are the little engines that could be such wonderful helper engines. They have all sorts of names, such as Billy and Jerry and Molly and Clarice and Helen and a host of others.

If they wanted to, you know, they could stand ready at the steep places, with steam all up, ready for service. Then, when they saw daddy or mother beginning to get tired under the strain, why, they could hitch right up with them and make their tasks much lighter.

I can think of all sorts of ways in which these little helper engines could give the main engines a big strong pull; and no doubt you can think of ways, too.

They could bring in the wood or the coal for the fire.

They could wash the dishes—and the kitchen floor sometimes.

They could make the beds, too—at least their own.

They could clean the bathtub and the basin.

They could cut the grass or water the flowers.

They could polish the shoes.

They could even do some of the washing and ironing, perhaps.

Oh, there are just a hundred or more ways in which the little helper engines could give the main engines a good hearty pull up the mountains of life—if they would!

Are you a helper engine? I wonder! What does mother say about it?

H. M. Lambert

A Dangerous Place to Play With a Sling!

66

Georgie's Glass House

GEORGIE was just getting over an attack of mumps. In fact, he had reached that stage of getting better when he was a bit cross and very hard to please. Perhaps you have felt the same way sometimes.

He was well enough to be up and about the house, though not quite well enough to go back to school At least, so the doctor said, although Georgie didn't think it was a bit fair.

"I don't see why I can't go to school!" he said crossly to his mother one morning, as he stood at the bedroom window watching the other boys and girls hurrying by. "I feel all right."

"All in good time," said mother. "Just another day or two now, and I know the doctor will say you can go. But it's better to be careful than sorry, isn't it?"

"No," snapped Georgie, "it isn't. I don't see why I can't go."

"Some day you will understand," said mother. "Now be a good boy and have a nice time with your toys."

But although Georgie had some beautiful toys, he had no desire to play with them. He wanted to go to school with his little friends, and everything else seemed horrid.

Left to himself, he began to look around for something to do. He felt he wanted something new and exciting, and seeing his slingshot lying among his toys, he suddenly had an idea.

"Now," he said to himself, "if only I had some pebbles

or pellets of some kind, I could really have some fun."

He began to look for odds and ends that would suit his purpose, and it was not long before his pocket was full of pieces of wood, tiny marbles, and some small lumps of coal. Then he went to mother's bedroom window, which faced the street, and settled down to enjoy himself.

His first victims were dogs and cats, which he sent yelping or mewing away as a well-aimed marble hit them. But he soon grew tired of this sport. Pretty soon an old man came along, wearing a tall hat. Maybe he was going to a funeral, but Georgie did not mind.

Ping! went a small lump of coal, and the poor man's hat toppled off to the pavement.

About this time Georgie remembered that the children would soon be coming back from school; he gathered up some more ammunition and waited.

"Here they come!" he said to himself after what seemed an age. "Now I'll surprise them."

He did. Boy after boy felt something hard hit him on the head or on his arm, and looking round, would shout at some other boy, thinking he was the one who had hit him. Sometimes a girl would scream as a mysterious something hit her on the leg; then she would turn angrily on the person behind her.

Nobody thought of looking up at the window of the fine home they were passing and, anyway, Georgie was being very careful to dodge down out of sight after every shot.

But you know, a boy can do a thing like this once too often. He may get away with it ten times, or even twenty times; but sooner or later he always gets caught.

Now a squabble was going on between a girl and two or three boys whom she was accusing of having thrown something at her. Suddenly, in the midst of the quarrel, a boy shouted, "Look, there he is! There's the fellow who's doing it! Why, it's Georgie!"

Of course, by the time everybody turned to look, Georgie had disappeared; but the open window was still there, while a piece of coal on the window sill completely gave him away.

Then the boys put their heads together and decided what they would do about it. Every one of them, just as soon as he got home, put his slingshot in his pocket so that he would be sure not to forget it in the morning.

Morning came and found Georgie at the window again. "If only they knew what was going to happen!" he chuckled to himself as he saw the children coming up the street.

Whizz! His first shot knocked a book right out of the hand of a little girl who was trying to read as she walked.

"What a perfect shot!" Georgie thought. "A simply perfect shot! Now for another."

Just then, however, something came whizzing through the window and hit the wall behind mother's bed. What could it be? thought Georgie, bobbing up just in time to feel something graze his head.

Ping! This one hit the bed itself.

Ping! Crash!

Another had hit a picture and the glass had splintered all over the floor. Georgie was frightened now. He bobbed up and cried, "You've smashed mother's picture!"

But nobody seemed to care.

Ping! Ping! Ping! All sorts of things were whizzing through the window now, and mother's bedroom began to look like a battlefield.

"Stop it! Stop it!" cried Georgie. "You'll break something else in a minute. And you've just hit me on the nose!"

At this there was a yell of laughter from the street; and now a marble came speeding on its way.

Bang! It hit the back of the mirror just hard enough to make an unsightly crack right across it.

"You bad boys!" cried Georgie. "You've broken—"

Just then the bedroom door opened and in rushed mother.

"What does all this mean?" she cried angrily as she strode across the littered floor to the window

At the sight of her face at the window, the boys ran for their lives.

"I asked, What does this mean?" said mother sternly, turning to Georgie.

"Those bad boys shot at me," said Georgie.

"Then I'll call the police."

"No—er—don't—not yet," gasped Georgie.

"Why not?" asked mother. And then she noticed the top of a slingshot sticking out of Georgie's pocket. She understood, very quickly indeed, as mothers always do.

"I think you had better close the window, dear," she said very firmly. Georgie closed it.

"Now give me the slingshot," said mother.

Georgie passed it over.

"Now get me your bank. It will take every penny you have to mend all these broken things."

With tears Georgie brought his precious money.

"Now take your—" began mother.

But do I need to go into detail about what happened next? Suffice it to say that Georgie got a very clear idea into his head as to what is meant by the old saying: "People in glass houses shouldn't throw stones."

Two Brave Firemen

THE trouble could not have come at a worse time. Father was away from home. Mother was still on crutches as a result of a bad accident she had been in some weeks before. Nine-year-old David and six-year-old Gordon were just getting over the measles, and Big Sister—well, she had just left for college that very afternoon.

Suddenly, as David looked out of the kitchen window, he saw smoke rising from behind the barn.

"Look," he cried to Gordon; "see that smoke? Whatever can be burning there?"

Then he remembered that the last thing Big Sister had done before she left was to carry out the hot ashes and dump them on the ash pile. Probably in her haste she had spilled some on the dry grass.

"Fire!" he cried. "Fire!"

"What's on fire?" cried mother from the next room, hobbling out on her crutches.

"Look, mother!" cried David. "The grass is on fire near the barn and the flames are spreading fast. See the smoke!"

Poor mother had never felt so helpless in all her life. Everything she owned was in danger, and yet, with her injured foot, she could do nothing.

"David, run for water, dear. Quick, quick!"

"Yes, mamma," cried David, grabbing two pails and running for the stream, which was at least fifty yards away.

Gordon grabbed another pail and in a flash was following his brother. Quickly they filled the pails and hurried back, pouring the water on the burning grass nearest the barn. Then back for more water, and back again to the fire.

It seemed a losing fight. What could two little boys do with three little pails and a great big fire?

"Keep it away from the gas tank!" cried mother. "See, it's going that way.

It was. Nearer and nearer it crept to the precious store of gas which father used for his tractor. If that should catch fire, then the house, barn, and everything might go.

The boys were getting tired now. It was so far to the stream! And it seemed farther every time they went down to it. Still they ran as hard as they could, and with every step they kept praying that Jesus would help them put the fire out.

Back they came with water to save the gas tank. And they saved it—just in time. Of course, they couldn't hope to stop the fire from going across the field—not with their three little pails—but they tried—oh, so hard—to keep it from creeping over to the barn and the house. And they won! The farm was saved.

Just as things were at their worst, and the boys were getting so tired that they felt they couldn't carry another pailful, the wind changed, blowing the fire down toward the stream, where, finally, it burned itself out.

Brave little firemen! Was mother proud of them? I should say she was! And so was father, too, when he got home and learned of all that they had done.

As for David and Gordon, they told me that they were sure they managed to beat the fire because of the little prayer they had prayed so often as they hurried to and from the stream with their pails.

The Voice That Was Lost— and Found

xxxxxxxxxxxxxxxxxxxxxxxxxxxxxxxxxxxxxxxxxxxxxxxxxxxxxxxxxxxxxxxxxxxxxxxxxxxxxxxx

THIS is a very remarkable story; so remarkable, in fact, that you may be tempted to say, "Aw, it couldn't have happened!" But I assure you that it really, truly, did.

Doris was just seven years old at the time, and getting along so well at school that mother was very proud of her. But Doris had one fault—she always wanted her own way no matter what mother said to her.

The problem came up again about the way Doris was to go to school. Because mother wanted her to go one way, but Doris wanted to go another way, there was a good deal of trouble in the camp.

"Darling," said mother one morning, "I wish you wouldn't take that short cut along the back streets. Sometimes the boys get very rough down there, and I don't want anything to happen to you. Please keep to the main streets and then everything will be all right."

"But, mamma," pleaded Doris, "those back streets are quite all right. I've looked down them so many times and they are almost always empty. It would save me such a lot of time if I could walk to school that way."

"It wouldn't save you more than five minutes altogether," said mother; "and I would rather you would take a little more time and be safe."

"Well, I don't see why I shouldn't go that way," said Doris in a grumbly tone of voice.

"Maybe not," said mother, "but, mind, I want you to keep to the main streets."

Doris, pouting a little, went off to school. And because mother's words were fresh in her memory, she went to school the long way round. But in the evening, when she was coming home, she began to think that after all *she* was right, not mother.

"I can't see why mamma doesn't want me to go home the short way," she said to herself. "Mamma just doesn't understand. If she were a little girl feeling as tired and hungry as I am, she'd take the short cut; I know she would."

So she argued with herself, finally feeling convinced that the short cut would be quite all right this afternoon.

It was. There was hardly anybody in the back streets, and feeling greatly pleased with her little self, Doris arrived home safely. But she didn't tell mother which way she had come.

The next afternoon it was just the same, and the next, and the next. Sometimes Doris smiled to herself as she thought of how frightened mother had been about the back streets. "She just doesn't know about them," she thought; but still she didn't tell mother what she was doing.

Then one afternoon it happened—the very thing of which mother had been afraid all the time.

As Doris walked home this time she noticed a group of boys outside a candy store. Since they were playing together quite happily, she did not give them another thought —at least, not until she was quite close to them. Then she saw that they were playing a rather rough game called "Dodgem," which, properly played, consists of throwing a ball at some chosen person; he is supposed to "dodge" it. Unfortunately, not having a ball, these boys were throwing old tin cans, rotten cabbages, and tomatoes—in fact, anything on which they could lay their hands.

Suddenly they spied Doris, who had moved for safety to the opposite side of the street.

"Dodgem!" they cried. "Dodgem!"

Then they started to throw things at her just as hard as they could.

Doris began to run, but it was no use. The boys could run as fast as she, and soon they were chasing her down the street like a pack of wolves, each one hurling at her whatever his hands could pick up from the street, all the time shouting, "Dodgem! Dodgem!"

But poor little Doris couldn't "dodgem," and soon her pretty frock was a sight!

Of course, nobody meant to hurt her, but suddenly Doris gave a scream, clutched her throat, and fell over in the roadway.

The boys crowded round, wondering what could have happened.

"Her throat is bleeding," said one of the biggest boys. "Somebody must have thrown a stone."

Somebody had, but no one would say who; and after all, what was the use of bothering about that now? The mischief had been done.

They tried to get Doris to say what was the matter, but she didn't reply. She couldn't. Then the boys became really frightened and one of them ran for a policeman. He picked Doris up in his strong arms and carried her home.

"Doris! what's the matter?" cried mother, as she opened the door. Doris! What has happened?"

Still Doris could not speak.

Mother, talking to her all the time, took her indoors and

bathed her throat; but Doris never said a word. She seemed to be trying to speak, but couldn't. Now mother became very much frightened and sent for the doctor. When he came he said that the stone had struck Doris's voice box and maybe she would never be able to talk again.

Some days later they both went to see a specialist, and he said just what the doctor had said. They came away from his office feeling very, very sad.

Doris would never be able to speak any more! Do you wonder that when mother was all alone, she cried and cried? Well, she did. And Doris thought—oh, how often!—how foolish she had been not to take mother's advice. What a price she had paid for her disobedience!

Months passed. The wound on Doris's throat healed, but she was still unable to say a word. By this time mother had begun to believe that she would never hear the dear, sweet voice of her little girl again.

Then one day there was another knock at the front door. Mother went to open it and found a man selling books.

"No," she said. "Not today, thank you."

"But they are children's books," he said. "Maybe you have a little boy or girl—"

Then mother thought of Doris and invited the man to step inside.

As soon as the man saw Doris, he brought out some of his books—I like to think that they may have been "Bedtime Stories"—and began talking to her about them. He asked Doris what she thought of the pictures, but there was no reply. Surprised, he turned to mother, but she merely put her finger on her lips and shook her head.

"Oh, I'm so sorry," said the man. "I didn't understand. Isn't there any hope?"

"None," said mother. "None at all. We have tried every doctor and every specialist we know."

"There is another who might help," said the man.

"Who is it?" asked mother eagerly.

"The Great Physician," said the man. "Have you tried Jesus?"

"No," said mother, hanging her head a little. "We haven't."

"Would you mind if I were to ask Him?" suggested the man.

"No, of course not," said mother, "if you wish."

So the stranger got down on his knees beside Doris and prayed—oh, so simply—that Jesus, in His great love, would make her better and give her back her voice if He so willed.

Then he arose from his knees, said good-by to them both, and went on his way. Mother told him to bring her some of the books when he should come that way again.

A week later he returned.

As he was walking down the street toward Doris's house, he saw a little girl running to meet him as fast as her legs would carry her.

"We are so glad you have come!" she cried, taking his hand in hers. "We have been waiting all the week for you."

"My dear!" he exclaimed. "Do I really hear you speak?"

"Oh, yes! yes!" she cried. "It happened just as you left. I ran after you to tell you, but you were too far away."

There were tears in all their eyes, I can tell you, as they talked over this wonderful thing that had happened; and then they got down on their knees and thanked the great Lover of children for what He had done for Doris.

H. M. Lambert

Grandma Was Putting a Stitch or Two in Ruth's Dolly

Grandma's Piano

RUTH just loved to stay at her grandma's house, for she always had a happy time there. Grandma was kind and good to her, telling her stories, mending her dolly's clothes, and of course, giving her nice things to eat.

Every Wednesday night grandma would put Ruth to bed early, then walk across town to Mrs. Henderson's house to attend prayer meeting. Except for illness or a very bad storm, grandma had not missed a prayer meeting in twenty years; and even now that she was "getting on in years," as she said, she was determined to be there, come what might.

One day, while Ruth and grandma were having a jolly little chat together, Ruth asked a question which seemed to puzzle the old lady quite a bit.

"Grandma," asked Ruth, "why do you have to go all the way to Mrs. Henderson's house for the prayer meeting? It's too far for you to walk nowadays."

"Well, darling," said grandma, "I don't think I have ever thought about it. We've all been going to Mrs. Henderson's house for years and years, and I suppose I shall keep on going there as long as I live."

"But, grandma," persisted Ruth, "why don't you have the prayer meeting in your house? Then you wouldn't have to walk anywhere!"

Grandma smiled. "I never stopped to think about it," said grandma, smiling. "Oh, yes, I did. I know. It's because I don't have a piano, and Mrs. Henderson does. So there you are, dear, that's the reason."

79

But if grandma thought that Ruth would be satisfied with that, she was mistaken.

"Grandma," said the little girl after a while, "why don't you have a piano in your house?"

"Because," said grandma, "I don't really need a piano. I could still play it, though, if I had one."

"But, grandma," said Ruth, "you really do need one; then you wouldn't have to go out in the cold and wet; and you wouldn't have to walk so far."

"I know, darling," said grandma, "but there's another reason—and a very important one, too. I couldn't afford to buy a piano if I wanted one. I think we had better leave things just as they are."

"But grandma," said Ruth, "couldn't Jesus give you a piano?"

"Of course He could," said grandma; "but I don't think He will because—well, as I told you, I don't really need one."

"But, grandma, you do need one," said Ruth, "and I am going to ask Jesus to send you one. Won't it be lovely when you have a piano of your very own, and the people all come here to the prayer meeting?"

Grandma smiled and sighed. She did not know what to say now. Not for a million dollars would she destroy Ruth's faith in the power and love of Jesus.

"Well, dear," she said finally, "we must leave it all to Him, mustn't we?"

"Oh, yes, grandma," said Ruth. "Of course we must, but I am going to ask Him to send you one."

And she did.

Morning by morning, and evening by evening, she sent up the sweet and loving petition, "Please, Jesus, send grandma a piano, so she won't have to go so far to the prayer meeting."

I don't know exactly how long it was before the answer came—maybe two or three weeks, maybe a month. Then one afternoon, as grandma and Ruth were sitting together in the dining room and grandma was putting a stitch or two in Ruth's dolly, they were suddenly aroused by strange sounds outside the front door.

Some men were shouting to each other.

"Heave-oh!" cried one. "Steady there," cried another. "Steady now. Take it easy, men. Take it easy."

Then the men seemed to be climbing the stairs to the front door, coming ever closer and closer.

Grandma stopped her work and looked up. "What is that?" she asked. "Who can be coming to see us this afternoon?"

"Steady now," came the voices again. "Take it easy. Let her down carefully. Don't let her fall. Careful now, careful."

Then there was a loud bang on the front door.

Ruth's eyes sparkled with excitement.

"Grandma!" she cried. "Perhaps it's your piano. Oh, grandma, let's go and see!"

Ruth flew across the room and opened the door.

"Grandma! It is! Jesus has sent your piano."

"I don't know who sent it," said one of the men; "but here it is, and what are we to do with it?"

"Bring it in; bring it in!" said Ruth, while grandma stood back wondering what all this might mean, but with a a little prayer of thankfulness in her heart.

They found out afterward that the piano had belonged to one of the prayer meeting ladies who was leaving town and who, not knowing what to do with it, had suddenly had the idea of sending it round to grandma.

So here it was at last! A real piano! Right in grandma's own house! No matter who sent it, or why, Ruth was absolutely sure that it had come in answer to her prayer. Grandma said she believed it had, too. And so do I.

Back From the Sea

NELLIE and Frankie were on their way to the beach for the afternoon. How happy they were! There was nothing they loved so much as playing in the sand or paddling in the warm, shallow water.

"Now let me remind you both of just one thing," said daddy as the car slowed down. "Remember that you are both wearing new shoes. Take them off as soon as you get on the beach, and be very careful not to lose them."

"Yes, daddy!" they cried. "We will." But their thoughts were far away—on the beautiful wavelets which were breaking softly on the shore.

Now the car had stopped. The door opened and out jumped the two excited children, who ran off toward the water at top speed.

As they reached the sand, Nellie remembered about her shoes and, taking them off, carefully laid them where she was sure she would be able to find them again. Frankie, however, in his eagerness to reach the ocean, quite forgot all about his promise until he was right down near the water. Then because he thought it was too far to go back, he just kicked off his shoes and socks, left them where they fell, and dashed on in.

What a wonderful time they had together! When they had paddled long enough, they built sand castles, ran races, then paddled some more. So busy were they with their play that they failed to notice the turn of the tide, or how the waves crept slowly but surely up the beach to where

Frankie's precious new shoes were lying. But the waves came on just the same.

By and by, all too soon, daddy called from far up the beach: "It's time to go home; we'll have to be going soon."

Then began the search for the shoes. Nellie found hers all right, because she had been careful to leave them in a safe place. But Frankie's shoes were nowhere to be found. In fact, he couldn't even find the place where he had left them. It was covered by the water!

They searched and searched, but it was no use. The shoes were not to be found. Daddy said that Frankie was a very careless little boy, and he would have to go home bare-footed. But Nellie said that she had a pair of slippers in the car and Frankie could wear them.

So that is how they returned home. Nellie in her shiny new shoes and Frankie in Nellie's slippers.

Frankie did not feel very happy about it, for he liked new shoes just as much as Nellie. And you can be quite sure that daddy did not feel happy about it, nor mother either, for they would have to find the money for another pair.

"Maybe we could go back in the morning," said daddy, "and have another look."

"What's the use?" said mother. "They will have been washed out in the ocean by now."

"Well, we might as well go," said daddy. "It won't do any harm to look once more."

So in the morning they all drove back to the beach again to search for Frankie's shoes.

This time, strangely enough, it was daddy and mother who got out of the car, while Nellie and Frankie remained inside. They said they wanted to stay behind a little while by themselves, but didn't say why. This was so unusual that daddy said they could if they wished; then he and mother started off without them.

Left alone, Nellie and Frankie knelt down by the back seat of the car and began to pray. Nellie, by the way, was just nine and Frankie, seven. But they believed that Jesus loves children and delights to help them when they get into trouble.

So together they sent up a little prayer that Frankie's lost shoes might be found! Six times they prayed the same prayer, over and over again.

Then they saw daddy and mother hurrying back to the car. They were smiling happily as though they had had good fortune.

They had.

"Look!" cried Nellie. "See what daddy has!"

"My shoes! My shoes!" cried Frankie.

Yes, there they were, and hardly damaged at all. Daddy had found them not a hundred yards from where he had stopped the car. How or why they happened to be just there, no one could tell, but everybody was thankful, especially Nellie and Frankie, who then told what they had been doing while daddy and mother were on the beach searching for the shoes.

Such a little thing to pray for, you say? I know. Just a pair of shoes! But why not? Jesus is interested in all the little things of our lives. Did He not say of the sparrow: "Not one of them is forgotten before God"? He did, and He added, too: "Ye are of more value than many sparrows." Luke 12:6, 7.

So we are not to hesitate to pray for little things as well as big things. Not one of our prayers—not a single one —is "forgotten before God."

H. M. Lambert

"I Knew Jesus Would Send It"

86

Katie, Chris, and the Christmas Tree

❊❊❊

IT was the day before Christmas, and still there was no Christmas tree in its usual corner in the dining room.

Katie and Chris had crept into the room day after day, hoping to see it there as they had in years gone by, but the corner was always empty. They waited and waited, expecting to find it there any minute, only to be disappointed every time they looked.

Now it was the very last day. They felt they couldn't wait any longer. They just had to ask mother about it, and so they did.

"Mamma," asked Chris, "aren't we going to have a Christmas tree this year?"

"This is Christmas Eve," added Katie.

Mother's face fell. She had dreaded this moment.

"Darlings, I'm so sorry," she said. "I'm afraid we won't have one this year. I asked daddy to bring us one, but he has been so busy he forgot all about it. He told me so last night, and now it's too late. We live so far from town we never could get one in time."

"Oh, mamma!" cried Chris. "We do love the pretty tree in the corner. It won't be the same without it."

"It's too bad," said mamma. "I'll have to make it up to you some other way."

"But we want the tree," said Chris.

"Yes, we want the tree," echoed Katie.

The two children ran away to share their grief. But there was nothing anybody could do about it—at least, it seemed that way.

Then as they talked together, Katie said, "Chris, if we were to tell Jesus about the tree, do you think He would send us one?"

"Maybe He would," said Chris.

So, without telling mother a word about it, they got down on their knees and told Jesus what was in their hearts, the thing they wanted most just then.

You may say, Fancy asking Jesus for a Christmas tree! I know. It does sound strange. But Jesus understands little children, and loves to have them tell Him all their hopes and dreams.

He likes to surprise them, too! I know He does.

That very evening, soon after Katie and Chris had gone to bed, there was a knock on the back door. Who should it be but the neighbor who lived on the farm next to theirs. He had a strange tale to tell.

Coming back from town that very evening, he told mother he had been stopped by a stranger and asked if he would take something to the home of Katie and Chris.

"I looked at him carefully," said the neighbor, "and tried to think who it could be; but it was nobody I had seen before; and I have lived here all my life and know everybody for miles around."

"That's strange," said mother. "But what did he give you to bring us?"

"That's the funny thing," said the neighbor. "He gave me a Christmas tree, of all things; and I'm sure you have one already."

"But we haven't!" cried mother. "And the children

want one so very much. This is too wonderful for words! Who could have sent it to us?"

"I don't know," said the neighbor, "but here it is—a very beautiful one, too."

At the words "Christmas tree," Katie and Chris—who had been listening hard all the time—came bounding out of bed to where mother and the neighbor were standing at the back door.

And there was the tree—the biggest and most beautiful Christmas tree they had seen in all their lives.

"Oh!" they cried together. "What a perfectly lovely tree!"

"I knew Jesus would send it!" said Katie.

"I knew He would, too," said Chris.

And Katie told me herself—she and Chris are both grown up now—that all her life she has never forgotten that wonderful night nor the thrill she felt as she realized that her prayer had been answered.

Too-Curious Connie

DADDY was supposed to be looking after his little
daughter while the rest of the family went shopping.
When he agreed to this arrangement, he thought he was
going to have a pleasant, quiet time reading the newspaper
while Connie played with her toys on the floor; but things
were not working out just as he had planned.

True, he was sitting in a comfortable chair, but he was
not reading. Instead he was looking at a little curly head
that had popped up underneath the newspaper.

"What is it now?" he asked.

"Daddy," said Connie. "Why do chickens lay eggs?"

"Oh, well," said daddy, "I don't know exactly; I suppose it's so that they can have baby chicks."

"How do they lay eggs?" asked Connie.

"How?" asked daddy. "How? I don't know how,
darling. They just lay them, I suppose."

The curly head disappeared and daddy read exactly two
more paragraphs. Then the head bobbed up again.

"Daddy, are the baby chicks in the eggs all the time?"

"Yes—er—no," said daddy. "Part of the time."

"How do the chicks get out of the eggs?" asked Connie.

"Oh, they—um—they peck their way out."

The curly head disappeared once more and daddy read
one more paragraph. Back it came again.

"Daddy!"

"Oh, you dear little spoiler of the peace," said daddy.
"What now?"

90

"How long does a big chicken have to sit on eggs before the little chickens—'

"Now look here, darling," said daddy. "Why do we have to go into all this chicken business now?"

"Because mamma says there will soon be some baby chicks in our chicken house."

"Oh, I see," said daddy.

"May I go and see the mamma hen, daddy?"

Daddy saw a ray of hope. "Yes, darling," he said. "Of course, you may. But don't go too near her; she's probably cross. Mother hens usually are."

"All right, daddy; I'll be careful," said Connie as she sped away.

Daddy settled down to his paper, with his feet comfortably resting on the hassock. Peace at last!

But not for long. In a few minutes he was disturbed by a frightful noise in the chicken house. He rushed outside— and what do you suppose he saw? Believe it or not—and it's really true—there was Connie sitting on the half-hatched eggs, while the mother hen, squawking with rage, was half running, half flying about the shed, darting every now and then at the poor, frightened child and pecking at her bare hands and knees.

"Looks as though I arrived just in time," said daddy, picking Connie off the eggs.

"But — I — only — wanted — to — to — see — if — I — could — hatch — them myself," said Connie between her sobs. "She didn't — need — to — make — such — a — fuss."

"I know you meant well," said daddy. "But sometimes, dear, it's just as well not to be too curious, especially about other people's business."

H. M. Lambert

They Told Jesus What Was on Their Hearts

When They All Come Home Again

xxxxxxxxxxxxxxxxxxxxxxxxxxxxxxxxxxxxxxxxxxxxxxxxxxxxxxxxxxxxxxxxxxxxxxx

THE big railway station was crowded. Hundreds of soldiers were making their way to a troop train, and many wives and children had come to see them off.

A fine big man in khaki was talking to his pretty wife, while a sweet little girl was holding fast to his hand. Suddenly he picked up the little girl in his arms and kissed her over and over again, put her down gently, then turned and ran for his train.

Maybe you can guess why he turned away so quickly. I think it was because he was afraid he might cry if he stayed too long, and soldiers mustn't cry.

Then I began to think of all the other people who have had to go away from their homes and their loved ones in these sad, sad years—all the little children who have had to leave their mothers and fathers and go to live with strangers, so as to be safe from the bombs; all the boys and girls who have had to leave their homes and go to strange places to work by order of some government or other; all the families which have been separated by the war for all sorts of reasons.

What a lot of sad people there must be in the world today! How many of them must be longing for their loved ones to come home again! How many dear children there must be whose hearts are aching for their mothers and daddies far away! How many mothers and daddies there must be, too, who would give everything they have just to see their boys and girls once more!

93

Wouldn't it be glorious if someone could suddenly make all the trouble end, and then say, "Now let everybody go back home!"

What a happy day that would be! A shout of joy would go up from all over the world such as has never been heard before. In millions upon millions of little homes people would say, "Just think, daddy's coming home!" or, "How wonderful! The children will be back next week!" or, "It's too good to be true! but we'll all be together again soon!"

I wish I could make this happen, don't you? It seems to me that it would be the greatest, grandest thing that anybody could do. But neither you nor I can ever do it. In fact, nobody in all the world could do it. Only Jesus. He can, and He will.

Maybe you haven't heard about it, but it's really going to happen someday. In His beautiful book, the Bible, Jesus has told us some of His plans.

To His disciples He once said: "In My Father's house are many mansions: if it were not so, I would have told you. I go to prepare a place for you. And if I go and prepare a place for you, I will come again, and receive you unto Myself; that where I am, there ye may be also." John 14:2, 3.

That means that He has prepared a place for you and for me. For your mother and daddy, too, and for all your brothers and sisters, and the little friends you love. He wants them all to be in heaven with Him and with each other.

Soon, as He said, He will come back to take us to that beautiful home He has made ready for us; and in that happy day all who have gone to sleep in death will be awakened by His lovely voice, and "we which are alive . . . shall be caught up *together* with them in the clouds, to meet the Lord in the air: and so shall we ever be with the Lord." 1 Thessalonians 4:17.

There is the promise again. We are going to be "together." Not separated. Not left lonely forever. All who love Jesus, all who have truly given their hearts to Him, are going to live with Him through all the years to come.

In that happy day, the Bible says, "God shall wipe away all tears from their eyes; and there shall be no more death, neither sorrow, nor crying, neither shall there be any more pain." Revelation 21:4.

And Jesus said Himself, "I will rejoice in Jerusalem, and joy in My people: and the voice of weeping shall be no more heard in her, nor the voice of crying." Isaiah 65:19.

Then there shall be no more wars, no more falling bombs, no more ugly sights or dreadful noises, no more things to frighten us or make us sad. Our loved ones will not leave us, never to return. There will be no more sad partings, no more saying good-by.

That is why the Good Book says that "God shall wipe away all tears"—for nobody will feel like crying any more. They will all be together forever and ever—as far in the future as you can think, and a thousand times as far again.

Oh, it's going to be wonderful when "they all come home again" into the everlasting kingdom of God!

I would like to be there and see it happen, wouldn't you? Just to see everybody so happy will be marvelous! Can't you imagine thousands of mothers and daddies clasping their children in their arms and crying out happily, "Darling, here you are at last!" And the children shouting, "Daddy, it's you! Mamma, it's you!" What joy they will feel as they see their parents again!

No wonder it says that "the ransomed of the Lord shall

return, and come to Zion with songs and everlasting joy upon their heads: they shall obtain joy and gladness, and sorrow and sighing shall flee away." Isaiah 35:10.

They will have something to sing about, won't they? And they will be so very, very happy that they will go on singing forevermore.

Are you planning to be there? I hope so. Jesus will be disappointed if you aren't. He will be looking for you in that glad day.

Courtesy, Dr. J. F. Gernhardt

UNCLE ARTHUR'S
BEDTIME STORIES

Twentieth Series

With Every Good Wish

To ....

From ....

V20A10

A. S. Maxwell

So Happy Among the Flowers

Uncle Arthur's
BEDTIME STORIES
(*TWENTIETH SERIES*)

BY ARTHUR S. MAXWELL

"Honor thy father and thy mother:
that thy days may be long upon the
land which the Lord thy God giveth
thee." Ex. 20:12.

REVIEW AND HERALD PUBLISHING ASSOCIATION

TAKOMA PARK, WASHINGTON, D. C.

PRINTED IN U. S. A.

CONTENTS

Copyright, MCMXLIII, by the
Review and Herald Publishing Association

PREFACE

SERIES TWENTY! Whoever would have thought —back in 1924—that "Bedtime Stories" would still be coming out in 1944! How the years have hurried by since the first few stories were written! Now there are five hundred of them. And we have lost all count of how many copies have been printed. It is over seven million, and the number is growing nearly half a million a year. They are published simultaneously in the United States, England, and Australia, and are to be found in every part of the English-speaking world. Translated into several foreign languages, they reach the children of many nations and tongues.

From far and near come letters written by children— and sometimes by their parents—telling us how much help and happiness they have received from these little books. One mother living in a lonely part of Western Canada sent us this beautiful little note the other day: "Our Bobby, now past seven, has been reared on 'Bedtime Stories' since he could understand what we said to him, and he has absorbed a great deal of good from them. I want to thank you for the part these stories have played in helping Bobby to 'grow in grace, and in the knowledge of our Lord and Saviour.'" May "Bedtime Stories" bring similar blessings to every home they enter.

This year, as in all the years gone by, we have sought to follow the rule that every story must be founded upon fact and every one must contribute in some way to the development of Christian character. That every reader, whether young or old, child or parent, may be greatly helped along life's way by this latest volume is the sincere prayer of

THE AUTHOR.

A. S. Maxwell

Big Brother and His "Little Shadow" on the Stump of the Old Pepper Tree

6

Little Shadow

WHEN you look behind you on a bright, sunny day, what do you see? A shadow, of course. And when you try to run away from it, what happens? It runs as fast as you do, doesn't it? You can't get away from it, try as hard as you may. And why? Because it's yours. It belongs to you.

Well, it was just like this with Ronald, only a little different. He had two shadows!

The first was the ordinary shadow that all boys and girls take along with them and the other was—can you guess?—yes, his own Little Sister! There was no possible way of separating them. Wherever he went, she went. Whatever he did, she did. Whatever he said, she said. That's why Ronald called her his "little shadow."

Did she bother him? No indeed. Ronald was glad to have a real, live shadow like this. A big bonnie boy of nine, he thought there couldn't be anybody in the world so sweet and pretty and dear as his little sister, while she, only four years old, looked up to him as the most wonderful big brother any little girl could have.

How they did follow each other about! You would think they were tied together with a piece of string; but they weren't. The thing that joined them was an invisible bond of love and devotion.

If Ronald started to climb a tree in the orchard, Little Sister would follow him up just as far as she could go.

7

If he picked an apple, she picked an apple, and when he slid down the tree, she slid down too.

Down by the gate was the stump of an old pepper tree, long since cut down. If Ronald sat on one branch of it, then Little Sister was sure to sit on the other.

If Ronald said, "I'm going to play in the sand pile," Little Sister would say, "So am I," and off they would go with their spades and buckets.

At play or at work they were always together. When Ronald went to sweep the front porch and steps, which was one of his daily jobs, Little Sister would take her brush along, too, and sweep as hard as he did. The only trouble in this case was that she didn't always sweep in the right direction, but Ronald didn't mind, for it was such fun to see her trying her best to help.

When Ronald watered the garden with his big watering can, along went Little Sister with her little watering can. They had a wonderful time together until their clothes and shoes were wetter than the plants and mamma had to call them in to get dry.

When Ronald would sit down to read a book, a few moments later along would come Little Sister with another book and sit down beside him. Of course, she couldn't read the book herself, but she just liked to appear to be doing the same as he was. The funny thing was that if Ronald started to read out loud, Little Sister would "read" out loud, too, only what she said was just any old chatter that came into her mind, and there was plenty of that.

It was Ronald's habit to say his prayers every morning; and just as surely as he ran to kneel down beside a chair, Little Sister would dash to the same chair and kneel down beside him. When he prayed, she prayed, and the angels must have bent low to catch every precious word that she said, even though she didn't ask for the right things every time.

But it was at meals that Little Sister's efforts to copy her big brother were funniest of all. She watched every move he made and promptly did the same, good or bad, polite or impolite. If Ronald forgot his good manners for a moment and put too much food into his mouth, then sure enough the next minute Little Sister's mouth would be bulging too. If Ronald, alas, started to eat with his knife, then Little Sister would quietly pick up a knife and start eating that way also, until mamma caught them both at it and told them how very rude it was.

Sometimes Ronald would say, "I don't like carrots and turnips for dinner." At once there would come an echo from across the table, "I don't like carrots and turnips for dinner." In fact, just as surely as Ronald grumbled at his food, Little Sister would grumble too, not because she liked only the things Ronald liked, but just to do as he did. If he turned up his nose at rice pudding, then she turned up hers—that is, as far as it would go, which wasn't very far, seeing it was so small.

Then one day Ronald suddenly came to realize how great a responsibility was his. Coming in from school, where he had been playing with some rather rough boys, he accidentally used a very naughty word. Instantly he heard it again, repeated by Little Sister. Of course, she hadn't the faintest idea what it meant, or whether it was good or bad, but coming out of her sweet, pretty lips it sounded simply terrible. Ronald was shocked. To think that he, who loved her so much, should have taught her to say such a naughty word!

He remembered then how she copied everything he said, how she was indeed his own "little shadow," and he made up his mind then and there that he must never say or do anything that would be a bad example to her. Just because she was willing to follow him anywhere, he must lead her in the right way. He began to see new meaning in some lovely words his daddy had taught him:

> "I would be true, for there are those who trust me;
>   I would be pure, for there are those who care;
> I would be strong, for there is much to suffer;
>   I would be brave, for there is much to dare."

"There are those who trust me," Ronald repeated to himself. "That must mean Little Sister, for nobody could ever trust me as she does. I must be true and pure and strong and brave for her sake."

And he surely tried his very best to keep his high resolve.

How Ronald Got Lost

▼▼▼▼▼▼▼▼▼▼▼▼▼▼▼▼▼▼▼▼▼▼▼▼▼▼▼▼▼▼▼▼▼▼▼▼▼▼

G O away!" said Little Sister. "Go away!"
"Why, what's the matter?" asked Ronald.

"Go away! I don't want to play with you any more."

"But why?" asked Ronald.

" 'Cos I don't," said Little Sister.

Now just what had happened I really don't know, but poor Little Sister was all out of sorts. Maybe she had got out of bed on the wrong side that morning. Maybe she had not gone to sleep early enough the night before. Maybe her breakfast was giving her indigestion. Anyhow, there she was, all in a huff because Ronald would not do something the way she wanted it done.

"So you don't want to play with me any more?" asked Ronald sadly.

"No," said Little Sister, "I don't. I don't ever want to play with you any more."

"All right," said Ronald. "Then I'll go away and you won't see me again for a long time."

"All right, I don't mind," said Little Sister with a toss of her pretty little head. "I am going to play all by myself in the sand pile."

With that she turned away and began to dig very fast with her spade, but not for long. In fact, it couldn't have been more than two minutes later that she began to feel dreadfully lonely. She looked around. Ronald was nowhere to be seen and the garden seemed quite empty without him.

Oh dear, she thought, maybe he *has* gone away.   Maybe he won't come back again.

"Ronald!" she called.   But there was no reply.

Now she was really frightened.   Where *could* he be? She started walking round the house, calling, "Ronald! Ronald!" every moment or so.   Still there was no answer. She went to the front gate and looked up and down the road, but there was no sign of Ronald anywhere.

How still everything was! how very quiet! how dreadfully lonely!

"Ronald!"

No reply.

She wandered along the garden paths, through the trees, around by the garage, looking everywhere and calling, calling, calling.   Still there was no answering cry.

Tears began to run down Little Sister's cheeks.   Her own dear Ronald had gone away and left her.   She was all alone.   And she herself had sent him away!   Oh dear, oh dear!   Why had she done it?   At last she came back to the house and walked slowly up the steps to the front door, sobbing quietly to herself.

"Hello, my little darling," said mamma, opening the door.   "Whatever has happened?   Have you hurt yourself?"

"Ronald has run away," wailed Little Sister, "and he won't come back again."

"Is that so?" said mamma, though she didn't seem nearly so worried as might have been expected.

"Yes," sobbed Little Sister; "he's lost, lost, and I'll never, never see him again."

"But how did he get lost?" asked mamma, setting Little Sister on her lap and wiping her tear-stained face.

"He got lost," began Little Sister, " 'cos—'cos—'cos I told him to go away. Boo-hoo-hoo!"

"You told him to go away!" said mamma with surprise.

"Yes, I told him I didn't want him to play with me any more. Boo-hoo-hoo."

"Don't you think that was very unkind of you?" asked mamma.

"Yes," said Little Sister, "I do. And now he's gone away."

"Nice little sisters don't say things like that to their big brothers," said mamma.

"I know."

"Well, if you are truly sorry, he might come back."

"Might he?" cried Little Sister, her face lighting up. "Might he really? I'm sorry, mamma, really I am. I'll never tell him to go away again, never."

"Well," smiled mamma, "if you will go down the garden and look behind the big oak tree you might find something—"

Without waiting for more, Little Sister leaped from mamma's lap and tore down the garden like a streak of lightning.

Suddenly there was a shriek of delight from behind the oak tree. She had found him. In fact, Ronald had been there all the time! A moment later the two children came rushing up the path again, hand in hand, laughing and shouting together, both radiantly happy, as though nothing had ever gone wrong.

H. Hofmann, Artist

Jesus Tells the Woman of Samaria About the Well That Never Runs Dry

14

No Marks on God's Glasses

MOTHER had been reading to Jerry out of the Bible. Tonight it had been the story of the woman of Samaria whom Jesus met at the well. They had just reached the place where Jesus says to the woman: "Whosoever drinketh of the water that I shall give him shall never thirst; but the water that I shall give him shall be in him a well of water springing up into everlasting life." John 4:14.

"What does that mean, mamma?" asked Jerry. "How could a well of water spring up? Don't you have to let a bucket down into it?"

"That's a good question," said mamma. "With most wells you do have to let a bucket down, or use a pump, to get the water up; but Jesus says that with His well it is different. The water flows up and over, all on its own, and it keeps on flowing forever."

"But how could it?" asked Jerry.

"Well, darling," said mamma, "this is just a beautiful picture of the love of God for us. His love never stops flowing. It's like a spring that bubbles up out of the ground that no one can stop or like a mighty river that never dries up. We can take all we want of it, bucketfuls and bucketfuls, and after we have taken all we can use there's just as much left as before. No matter how many good things we may receive from Him today as proof of His love, we may know He is ready to bless us even more tomorrow and the next day and the next day after that, always and always."

"Just like you love me?" asked Jerry.

"Yes, darling, just like that," answered mamma, "only ever so much more. And that reminds me of a story I must tell you."

"Do!" exclaimed Jerry with eagerness, for he loved stories.

"It's about a poor boy who was brought to a hospital the other day. We'll call him Charlie, though that isn't his real name. He was very pale and thin. The doctor said he was half starved, and ordered that he be given plenty to eat to make him well again.

"The nurse brought him a big glass of milk and told him to drink it. But Charlie, looking up anxiously into her face, asked her, 'How deep do I drink?'

" 'How deep!' asked the nurse. 'Whatever do you mean?'

" 'Well, nurse,' said Charlie, 'at home all four of us children have to share the same glass of milk, and mother tells me to drink first because she knows I won't drink too much, and I know where the mark is for me to stop drinking.'

" 'You poor little thing,' said the kindhearted nurse. 'I understand, but you don't have to worry about that here. You may drink all of this. You don't have to watch for any marks.'

"So Charlie drank a whole glassful of milk for the first time in his life. Then he had more and more, for there was no end to the supply of milk the nurses wanted to give him after that.

"And so it is, Jerry," continued mamma, "with the love of God. It is like an everflowing well from which we can keep on drinking without ever fearing that we shall take too much. And when God offers His love to us He doesn't say, 'Drink some of it,' but 'Drink all of it.' And we may be sure that while there is sufficient for all our needs, there is just as much for everybody else in the world.

"There are no marks on God's glasses."

E. Galloway

It Wasn't Fido or Tommy Who Picked Mamma's Flowers

18

Who Picked Those Flowers?

WINIFRED was such a dear little girl! So sweet and beautiful indeed that everybody loved her. They loved her blue eyes and her curly hair and all her charming little ways. But there was one bad thing about her, and that was very bad indeed. She *would* tell her mamma wrong stories! Think of it! How very terrible!

Just as surely as mamma would come across some piece of mischief that Winifred had been up to, the little girl would say, so innocently, "I didn't do it, mamma, really I didn't." And all the time mamma knew perfectly well that she had done it.

Somehow Winifred could never bring herself to own up when she had done something that she shouldn't. She would either deny it outright or else think up some story about her brother or the little boy next door and blame them.

Just as though she could deceive her mamma indeed! What little girl ever could do any such thing? Mammas know so much about them that they had far better tell the truth right away.

But Winifred couldn't or wouldn't do that, and mamma wondered just what to do about it. She had made Winifred stand in the corner, she had told her to sit on a hard chair for a while; she had talked to her by the hour, telling her how very wicked it is to tell a lie; but nothing seemed to make any difference. So mamma made up her mind

19

that the very next time it happened she would try some other plan, if she could think of one.

Well, before long it did happen again. Mamma was out in the garden, looking at her flower bed. There was something strange about it. "I wonder why all those flowers are lying on the ground?" she said to herself. "And the stems are all left behind!"

"Winifred," she said solemnly, as the little girl came running up, "did you pick all these flowers?"

Winifred looked at the mess with seemingly great surprise.

"Why, no, mamma," she said. "Who could have done it? Maybe it was Fido, or maybe Tommy. He was playing in the garden yesterday."

Now mamma knew perfectly well that Fido would never bite the tops off flowers, and that Tommy had not been in the garden long enough to do so much damage.

"I think we'll go indoors," she said, and Winifred turned a little pale at the tone of her voice.

"Are we going to have supper now?" asked Winifred.

"Yes," replied mamma. "You may sit up in your place at the table."

"May I have my milk in my china cow?"

"Not this evening," said mamma.

"Why?"

"Because the cow won't want to give any milk to little girls that tell wrong stories."

Winifred was silent for a while. Then she asked, "Can I have some butter on my bread?"

"I'm sorry," said mamma, "but the butter just won't come out of the cupboard. It just won't come, that's all."

"Why?"

"You know why."

"Can't I have some honey on my bread?"

"Sorry," said mamma, "but the honey won't come out either. It just doesn't want to come."

"Why?"

"You know why."

There was another long silence. Then, "May I have a piece of cake?"

"I'm afraid not," said mamma, "for the cake says that it likes to be eaten only by good girlies who always tell the truth."

A tear began to trickle down Winifred's cheek. All her little world seemed to be standing still. All the nice things that had always happened so regularly had stopped happening. Maybe they would never happen again.

"It's bedtime now," said mamma. "Run along upstairs."

"Am I going to get a story tonight?"

"Not tonight, dear. You see, nobody wants to tell stories to little girls who—"

This was too much. Suddenly the tears began to flow like two great rivers.

"Boo-hoo-hoo! I picked the—flowers—mamma," Winifred said between her sobs. "I'm sorry. And —I—won't—ever—tell you—any more—wrong—stories. Really I won't, ever."

And to tell you the truth, she really did try hard to keep her promise.

Chickabit's Babies

CHICKABIT was a little Bantam hen. At the time all this happened—and it really did happen—she was sitting on some pretty little Bantam eggs, waiting hopefully for some fluffy wee chicks to come out of them.

Then, to her amazement, something most extraordinary took place. Instead of hovering fluffy little Bantam chicks she found herself sitting on two bantam puppies! At least, they looked like bantams, they were so very, very tiny. And this is how it happened.

Tommy, the boy who owned Chickabit, was a great lover of animals, and on hearing that a litter of pups had just been born at a near-by farmhouse, he had gone off to see them. Arriving there he had learned that the farmer did not want the puppies and was actually going to drown them all. So Tommy had begged for two of them and brought them home.

The pups were only two hours old when Tommy got back with them, so he had to start feeding them out of a nursing bottle. The question of how to keep them warm came up, for it was wintertime and if they were to get chilled they would die.

Tommy had an idea. Chickabit! His own precious Bantam hen. If she could keep eggs warm and little chicks warm, maybe she would keep the puppies warm too. But would she take them?

Tommy made a comfy little nest for Chickabit beside the woodstove in the kitchen and put the Bantam hen into it. Then he slipped the two little puppies under her wings.

Chickabit clucked her loudest, spread her wings in her most important-looking manner, and settled down to mother her two strange babies.

For two weeks Chickabit cared for the two growing pups. Then, alas, first one died, and then the other. It wasn't Chickabit's fault. Oh, no. She did her best for them and loved them as if they had been her very own. Why they both died I do not know. Tommy says he never found out.

Now that both the puppies were dead, Chickabit was put out in the yard again; but would she stay there? Indeed no. Every time the back door was opened, she dashed in and hurried over to the corner by the wood stove where she had been so happy with her little puppies.

One day the most amazing thing happened. Chickabit, having managed to get indoors again, was strutting about from one room to another as though searching eagerly for something. Suddenly she spied a small china dog on top of the piano in the living room. Instantly she flew up onto the piano and, folding her wings around that china dog, clucked gleefully as though at last she had found what she had been looking for so long.

Poor little Chickabit! How she must have loved those puppies!

"I Don't Want to Hold Hands," Said Betty

24

Holding Hands

BETTY was in one of those "grown-up" moods which made things difficult for everybody. From the way she was talking to her mamma as they walked down the street together, one might have thought she was three or four times her age—as old as her mamma, in fact.

"Betty," mamma was saying, "please take my hand; you might get lost in the crowd."

"No," said Betty, "I don't want to."

"Betty," persisted mamma, "I said, please take my hand."

"No," said Betty again, "I'm a big girl now and I don't have to take people's hands any more."

"Betty, you are just a little girl of five, and all nice little girls of five like to take their mamma's hands when they are out walking together."

"I don't want to be a nice little girl," said Betty. "I'm a grown-up girl and I don't hold hands when I'm out. Big people don't."

Mamma made a grab for Betty's hand and held it firmly for a while, but it wasn't very comfortable, with Betty making faces and squirming about trying to get her hand free. People began looking, and that didn't make mamma feel very happy inside.

"You'll be sorry, Betty, for behaving like this in public," said mamma. "And if you don't take my hand as I ask you to, something dreadful may happen to you."

"No, it won't," said Betty. "I'm a big girl and can

look after myself." And with that she yanked her hand free and walked on by herself with her head in the air.

"It's lucky for you," said mamma, "that we are not nearer home than we are. But we shall be there soon."

Betty did not seem to worry about what might happen to her when she got home. She was enjoying her foolish little dream, quite sure she could get along all right without her mamma.

They walked on together for some distance, Betty keeping just far enough away from mamma so she wouldn't have to take her hand.

Then they came to a wide crossing, with lots of cars and buses passing to and fro.

"You simply must take my hand now," said mamma firmly, making another grab at Betty. "I will not let you go over this busy street by yourself, however big you think you are."

They waited for the lights to change. At least, mamma did. Betty was too anxious to be big and free. When she saw a break in the line of traffic, she quickly slipped her hand out of mamma's and started off on her own, walking very fast so that mamma would not be able to catch her. But the light ahead was still red and the cars were still rushing by.

Suddenly there was a tooting of horns, a screeching of brakes, and the shrieking of women who saw a little girl lying in front of a bus. Everybody crowded round; the policeman came, and the ambulance men. In less time than it takes to tell, Betty was being hurried off to the hospital, with mamma sitting in the ambulance beside her.

Fortunately, Betty was more frightened than hurt, for the bus driver had seen her in time and had been able to stop without running over her. But she was plenty frightened all right!

Presently a little hand came out from under the covers and reached for mamma's. "I like holding your hand, mamma," said Betty. "Really I do. It makes me feel better all over."

Mamma took the little hand and squeezed it tightly. She knew then that she wouldn't have any more trouble with Betty about holding hands.

H. A. Roberts

Betty Learned It Was Safer to Take Her Mother's Hand Than to Walk Out Alone

How Dozy Joe Woke Up

TEACHER had her eye on Joe. There was something the matter with him, but what it was she could not make out.

There he was again with his eyes shut and his head on his hands, and it was only ten o'clock in the morning!

"Joe, wake up!" called the teacher, and Joe sat up with a jerk.

"Yes, Miss Lambert," he said, and started to look at his book again. But it was of no use, he couldn't seem to get any meaning out of the words and his head *would* keep nodding.

Joe was always sleepy; at least, so it seemed to the teacher, and the children in the class seemed to think the same, for they had given him the nickname of "Dozy Joe." He was too sleepy even to play. When it came time for games, Joe just sat and watched. When he did take part in them, he played so poorly that the others were glad when he dropped out. No leader ever clamored to have Joe on his side. Nobody wanted him. He was too dozy.

As for his schoolwork, it was as bad as his play. He couldn't seem to learn and, of course, his marks were terrible. In almost every subject he was at the foot of the class.

The next time the teacher sent a report home to Joe's mother she added a few remarks. "Joe is always sleepy," she wrote. "He does not seem able to do good work. I fear there may be something the matter with his health or his habits. Perhaps he should see a doctor."

"The idea!" said Joe's mother. "There's nothing the matter with my Joe. Why, he never goes out of the house after he gets home from school."

All the same, she made up her mind to watch Joe for a while to see whether anything was wrong with him. "Maybe," she said to herself, "I haven't been keeping my eye on him as much as I should."

When Joe arrived home from school the next day, mother noticed that he went straight to the radio and turned it on. Then he made himself comfortable in front of the loud-speaker and listened with eager interest.

Mother didn't think much of this, for she had often noticed Joe in front of the radio, but when, an hour later, she discovered he was still there, she thought perhaps he had been there long enough.

"Joe," she said, "are you still at that radio?"

"Yes," said Joe. "There's a wonderful story on now. It's about a battle between a plane and a submarine. Mum, the guns are just blazing away, can't you hear them?"

"Well, Joe, don't spend too long there."

"All right, mum," said Joe, and settled down again to enjoy the story. Half an hour passed.

"Joe!" cried mother. "Didn't you hear me call you for supper?"

"No, mum."

"Come along, right away. Everything is spoiling."

Slowly Joe made his way into the kitchen and sat down at the table. As soon as he had finished he started to slip away to the radio again.

"Where are you going?" asked mother.

"There's another story coming on in a few moments," said Joe.

"But you haven't done your homework," said mother.

"I know, mum," said Joe. "I'll do it just as soon as this story is over. It's a serial and I've been listening to it every evening now for some time and I mustn't miss it. It's simply wonderful, mum. You'd like it, too. It's so exciting."

"Oh, I see," said mother, beginning to understand. "Well, you may listen to it tonight, but remember that homework must be done without fail. And now I have to go next door to see Mrs. Jones. Be sure to be started by the time I get back."

It must have been an hour later when mother got back. Joe was still seated by the radio. When he saw mother, he jumped up and hurried toward his books.

"Joe!" cried mother. "What do you mean! The evening is almost gone and you have been listening to the radio the whole time. How can you expect to do your homework properly now?"

"I'll get it done all right," said Joe with a big yawn.

"You can't," said mother. "You are too sleepy. You won't learn a thing tonight. You might just as well go to bed."

"But I've *got* to do it," said Joe, yawning again.

"Then why didn't you do it when you first got in from school?"

"I had to listen to my program," said Joe.

"No, indeed," said mother firmly. "You have had enough program to last you for a long time. You can't hope to listen to stories and jazz and what not hour after hour and then do a good job with your schoolwork. You are just making yourself addlepated, that's what you are."

"Apple what?" asked Joe.

"I didn't say anything about apples," said mother. "I said you are making yourself addlepated—addled like a bad egg—muddled, stupid. That's why you are so sleepy at school all the time."

"I don't think so," responded Joe.

"But I do," said mother, "and we're going to try a new program from now on. We'll keep the radio off for a few days and see what happens."

"You mean I can't listen any more?"

"That's exactly what I do mean," replied mother. "You will do no more listening until you are getting good marks in class again."

"Oh!" groaned Joe.

But mother was firm as a rock. For a whole week and more the radio was kept turned off when Joe was at home. The time he had spent listening he now began to spend on his studies. Soon a note came from teacher.

"Joe is showing marked improvement," it said. "He is taking a new interest in his work."

Somehow Joe had new energy for his play as well. He began to do his best to win, like the others. Captains chose him. His help was valued.

Dozy Joe was awake at last.

"I Want to Say Mine First," Said Barbara

32

Trouble at Prayer Time

"I WANT to say my prayers first," said Barbara.

"No," said mamma, "Freddie says his prayers first, and you second."

"Why?" wailed Barbara, beginning to cry.

"Because Freddie is your big brother and he always says his prayers first."

"But I want to say my prayers first."

"But prayer isn't a game, darling," explained mamma patiently. "It is talking to Jesus, and we mustn't quarrel about that, must we?"

"But I want to say mine first," insisted Barbara. "And if I can't, then I won't say them at all."

"Well," said mamma, "Freddie has said his prayers already, so why not say yours now anyway?"

"I don't want to."

"Oh, come along, darling," urged mamma. "Be a good girl. Now let's begin. 'Gentle Jesus.'"

"'Gentle Jesus.' Boo-hoo-hoo!"

"Don't cry like that, dear."

"But I want to say mine first."

"I thought we had got past that, dear," said mamma. "Come along now. 'Meek and mild.'"

"'Gentle Jesus, meek and mild.' Boo-hoo-hoo!"

"That's better. 'Look upon.'"

"'Look upon a little child.' Boo-hoo."

And so it went on right down to "Give this little child a

place." Then, still weeping, Barbara crawled into bed and put her tear-stained face down on the pillow.

"Do you know what I think about that prayer?" said mamma, as she tucked in the bedclothes.

"No."

"Well, I don't think Jesus liked it very much, that is, if He was able to hear it at all."

"Why couldn't He hear it?"

"Because there was too much noise—nobody could make out what you were saying."

Barbara didn't reply. She seemed to be thinking about that.

Presently mamma kissed her good night and started to leave the bedroom.

"Mamma!" cried Barbara. "Come back."

"What for?"

"About my prayer, mamma. If you think Jesus couldn't hear it, maybe I ought to say it over again."

"That's a very good idea," said mamma. "I'll stay with you while you do."

So Barbara tumbled out of her cozily tucked-in bed and got down on her knees once more. This time there was no crying and she went all the way from "Gentle Jesus" to "child a place" without a break.

"That's the way, darling," said mamma, as she kissed Barbara good night once more. "Only wouldn't it have been much better to say it that way the first time without all that fuss?"

"I suppose it would," admitted Barbara, as she snuggled down into bed and went to sleep.

How Mildred Missed the Party

THIS is a strange story if ever there was one. It's about a little girl who would keep tearing her dresses.

Now just think of that! Fancy a little girl tearing her dresses! You could imagine a boy tearing his trousers, or even his shirt, but a little girl tearing her dresses, why, that's dreadful!

And it isn't as though she just tore her play dresses or her school dresses. She tore her Sabbath and her party dresses—in fact, every dress she had.

Just how it happened I don't know, but as sure as Mildred had a new dress given to her, she would somehow get a hole in it. She didn't mean to, of course; she didn't want to; but the tears came just the same.

What a careless girl! you say. Yes, indeed! That's what her mamma said, but it didn't keep the dresses from being torn. Something terrible had to happen first.

One day daddy came home with a very beautiful party frock in his bag. He liked buying dresses for Mildred, although he never could understand why she wore them out so soon.

This was an unusually pretty dress, and mamma said he had paid much too much for it, and that it was only to be used for some very special occasion, such as a Christmas party or a wedding. So it was hung up carefully in Mildred's closet to await the proper time for her to use it.

But Mildred had other ideas. When she was all alone in her room, she took the dress out of her closet and put it on—just to see how she looked in it, of course. For some time she gazed in the mirror admiringly and then, very pleased with her little self, she began dancing round her bedroom. Round and round she went, faster and faster. So excited did she become that she bumped into the door and caught the handle in one of the puffed sleeves.

Zzzzz! There was an ugly tearing sound. Mildred stopped suddenly and shuddered as she guessed what had happened.

Quickly she took off the dress and examined the tear. There it was at least three inches long. She tried to smooth it down so that it would not be so easily noticed, but in her nervousness she tore it some more. Then, hearing mamma coming up the stairs, she slipped the dress quickly on its hanger and put it back in the closet.

Mildred held her breath as mamma went to the closet and removed two or three other dresses, which she took downstairs to mend. Would she see the tear in the new dress? Would she guess something had happened to it?

No, mamma did not notice it, and Mildred made up her mind that she would just keep quiet and say nothing about it.

Weeks passed and the new dress, with its ugly tear, was almost forgotten. Then, all of a sudden, came an invitation to a very special party. Alice Ann, Mildred's best friend, was asking a number of girls to her home, and would Mildred come too?

How exciting! There was no place in the world that Mildred loved to go more than to Alice Ann's beautiful home.

Mamma was perfectly willing. "Isn't it fortunate," she

said, "that you have that nice new party dress to wear, that daddy brought you?"

"May I wear that?" asked Mildred. "Oh, how perfectly wonderful!"

Suddenly she felt very frightened as she remembered the tear in the sleeve.

Should she tell mamma? She couldn't. The words just wouldn't come.

The day wore slowly by, and the next, and the next, until at last the day of the party arrived. Still Mildred had not said anything about the tear. And the longer she put it off, the harder it became to speak of it.

"What time does the party begin?" asked mamma.

"Five o'clock," said Mildred, "and Bob is calling for me in his car. He is picking up several of the girls, and he says he will be here at four-thirty sharp and I am to be all ready."

"Well, there's one good thing about it," said mamma, "with that brand-new frock to wear, it won't take you long to get dressed. No mending this time, for once."

"No, mamma," said Mildred meekly, but with a growing sense of trouble ahead.

Of course, it wasn't possible to keep the secret much longer. Mamma went upstairs just before four o'clock to make sure Mildred was getting along all right, and there it was lying on the bed—the lovely new dress with the great gash in the sleeve.

"Mildred!" cried mamma. "Whatever have you done now! You don't mean to say you've torn this dress too! And you haven't even worn it yet!"

Then it all came out, as things like this always do; and mamma said that Mildred could not possibly go to the party with a big tear in her dress and there wasn't time to mend it.

While they were still talking together the doorbell rang. It was Bob, with a carful of happy, laughing girls.

"Ready, Mildred?" he called. "Hurry up! We're late."

But Mildred wasn't ready, and the car went on, while a little girl in a white petticoat stood at the top of the stairs feeling very, very sorry for herself and promising her mamma that she really wouldn't tear her dresses any more.